Preface

This short text is an attempt to provide a revision text for medical undergraduate and postgraduate students and others who require a brief resumé of the subject. The chapters on basic immunology contain a few selected examples of applications to clinical problems to emphasise the value of the material in interpreting disease states.

After nearly 40 years of research into the basic mechanisms of humoral and cellular immunity, the science of immunology has come round almost full circle back to its origins in infection and immunity. This is reflected in Chapter 6, the focus of the book.

The coverage is by no means comprehensive, but in the author's view the key areas of the subject are dealt with in sufficient detail to enable the reader to apply the information to a wide range of immunological problems.

For those who require more detailed information a number of up-to-date texts are available, including the beautifully illustrated *Immunology* by I. Roitt, J. Brostoff and D. Male published by Churchill Livingstone Gower in 1985. This book covers both basic and clinical information, combining the resources of two dozen prominent immunologists. The 5th edition of *Basic and Clinical Immunology*, edited by D. P. Stites. J. D. Stobo. H. H. Fudenberg and J. V. Wells and published by Lange in 1984, provides even more extensive coverage of this area. *Immunology Today*, produced monthly by Elsevier Science Publishers, includes news, features and review articles that are invaluable to immunologists in keeping abreast with new developments and views in this rapidly developed field.

Edinburgh, 1986   D. M. W

Aids to Immunology

D. M. Weir
MD, FRCPEd
Professor of Microbial Immunology, Department of Bacteriology,
University of Edinburgh; Honorary Consultant Immunologist,
Lothian Health Board, Edinburgh, UK

CHURCHILL LIVINGSTONE
EDINBURGH LONDON MELBOURNE AND NEW YORK 1986

CHURCHILL LIVINGSTONE
Medical Division of Longman Group UK Limited

Distributed in the United States of America by
Churchill Livingstone Inc., 1560 Broadway, New
York, N. Y. 10036, and by associated companies,
branches and representatives throughout the
world.

First published 1986
Reprinted 1990

ISBN 0-443-03562-8

British Library Cataloguing in Publication Data
Weir, D. M.
    Aids to immunology.
    1. Immunology
    I. Title
    616.07′9   QR181

Library of Congress Cataloging in Publication Data
Weir, D. M. (Donald Mackay)
    Aids to immunology.
    Includes index.
    1. Immunology. I. Title.
QR181.W388   1986   616.079   86–13619

Produced by Longman Singapore Publishers (Pte) Ltd.
Printed in Singapore

Aids to Immunology

WITHDRAWN

Contents

Contents

1. Essential features of immunity

Immunity exists in *natural (non specific)* and *acquired (specific)* forms.

Natural immunity
This depends on a variety of features of the make up of the host tissues and body fluids and is independant of any prior contact with foreign agents, such as bacteria or viruses. This form of immunity will be described in Chapter 6 on host defences against infectious agents.

Acquired immunity
This is the subject of most present day studies in immunity and depends on contact between the cells of the hosts immune system and foreign agents called **antigens**—these may be microorganisms (or their products) of even entirely bland substances that are not components of the hosts own tissues.

ACQUIRED IMMUNITY

1. Two major categories of response: **humoral immunity** and **cellular immunity**
2. Both are essential components of defences against pathogenic microorganisms.
3. **Humoral immunity** is mediated by serum gamma globulins called *antibodies* (or *immunoglobulins*)
4. **Immunoglobulins** are synthesised by a class of white blood cells called *B-lymphocytes*. These cells originate from stem cells in the bone marrow and the antibodies (immunoglobulins) they secrete are found throughout the blood and in many body secretions
5. Each antibody immunoglobulin is **specific** for the foreign antigen that induced its formation
6. **Cellular immunity** is mediated by another class of lymphocytes called *T-lymphocytes* and a class of phagocyte called *macrophages* (or monocytes). T-lymphocytes like B-lymphocytes originate from bone marrow stem cells but differentiate in the *thymus gland* before emigrating to the peripheral tissues

ANTIGENS

Their essential characteristic is that they are foreign to the host—for example, rabbits will make an immune response against *human albumin* but not against *rabbit albumin* and vice versa. Chemically the two albumins are very similar but the small differences that exist in parts of the molecule are sufficient to stimulate an *immune response*.

Characteristics

1. Normally foreign to the host
2. May be microorganisms or their products
3. May be bland substances—e.g. serum proteins of another species
4. Normally high molecular weight substances—e.g. over 10 000 Daltons
5. Low molecular weight substances can induce an immune response if attached to a *carrier molecule*, such as a serum protein. Such low molecular weight substances are called **haptens**
6. Antigens that can induce an immune response alone (i.e. without being attached to a carrier molecule) are called *immunogens*
7. An **immunogen** is usually a complex molecule with many structures within the molecule that are foreign to the host. The immune response of the host is then directed against each of the foreign structures (or *antigenic determinants*)—some more than others, depending on their accessibility (see below) and degree of foreignness. An antigenic determinant is sometimes called an epitope
8. The more foreign (i.e. different from substances in the host tissues) the stronger the immune response to the antigenic determinant

Chemical nature

1. Most biological substances are *complexes* of different classes of chemicals—proteins, carbohydrates, lipids and nucleic acids. Any of these classes of compound can be immunogenic (i.e. act as an immunogen) unless they are of low molecular weight (see above—*Haptens*). Proteins and carbohydrates are usually more immunogenic than lipids and nucleic acids.
2. *Denaturation* (either chemical or other, such as heat) of a molecule changes its chemical configuration, so that the antibody immunoglobulin which reacted to the native material will no longer recognise it.
3. The *determinants* that induce an immune response to a complex molecule have to be accessible to the cells of the immune system and therefore are usually on the surface of the molecule
4. Readily accessible determinants tend to induce a more

powerful immune response and are called *immunodominant determinants.*

5. Many foreign molecules are broken down by enzymes in the host so that *internal determinants* are exposed to the immune system. Therefore antibodies to such internal determinants will not react with the native molecule, when tested in an *in vitro* system.

6. The *charge* of a molecule is not a crucial determinant of immunogenicity as completely uncharged molecules, such as dextran, can be shown to be immunogenic.

7. In contrast, the *optical* configuration of a molecule appears to affect its immunogenicity—e.g. D-amino acids that are poorly degraded because of their resistance to proteases and are also poorly immunogenic.

CLINICAL CONSIDERATIONS

1. Drugs
Some drugs e.g. antibiotics can act as immunogens but often need first to combine with a tissue component i.e. they behave as haptens. Penicillin and sulphonamides can behave in this way and this is important in what are termed hypersensitivity states (Ch. 8)

2. Foreign tissues
Foreign tissues (*grafts*) or cells (e.g. *blood cells*) can act as immunogens. The immune response results in graft rejection or destruction of the foreign red blood cells. Determination of compatibility is therefore an important prerequisite before foreign tissue or cells are administered.

Tissue transplants—grafts
1. A *transplant* involves the transfer of live tissue or cells (e.g. kidneys, bone marrow) from one individual to another
2. *Grafts* are given different names according to their source:
   Autografts are from another part of the same individual
   Isografts or *syngeneic grafts* are donated by another member of the same strain
   Allografts are obtained from another individual of the same species (not inbred)
   Xenografts are donated by another species
3. Only isografts and autografts are unlikely to be rejected
4. Rejection of the other types of graft depends on:
   (a) the closeness of the relationship between the antigens of the recipient and the antigens of the graft (match)
   (b) the success of immunosuppressive measures
5. Grafts from inbred strains (isografts)—from one parent to their F_1 offspring—will express the antigens of both parents

Graft rejection mechanisms
1. *Allograft* rejection is due to T-lymphocytes (Tc and Th) reacting against the *major histocompatability (MHC) gene products*—mainly Class 1 antigens—present on the transplanted cells
2. Graft *rejection can be transferred* from one individual to another by intravenous injection of living lymphoid cells from an immune donor. Serum transfer in ineffective.
3. *Accelerated* rejection takes place when repeated grafts are made (second set response) due to the development of *acquired immunity*

Transplantation antigens
These are graft antigens and are sometimes called histocompatibility antigens. They are:
(a) Coded for in man by a gene complex called the major histocompatibility complex (MHC) situated on Chromosome 6. The antigens are called HLA antigens—*human leucocyte antigens* as they are normally typed in the laboratory on peripheral blood leucocytes. The *HLA-type* of an individual is sometimes associated with disease (Ch. 9)
(b) In the mouse, the gene complex is situated on Chromosome 17 and the antigens are called *H-2 antigens*
(c) The antigens are found in the membrane of cells and exist as transmembrane glycoproteins (Fig. 4.2)
(d) Certain of these antigens—HLA-A and HLA-B in man and H2-K and H2-D in mouse—are the main determinants of graft rejection

Figure 4.1 shows a simplified view of the gene complexes in man and mouse.

3. Auto antigens
In certain disease states the hosts own tissues can act as immunogens. These disease states are called *autoimmune diseases* in which the immune response is directed against self rather than foreign antigenic determinants (ch. 9). Autoimmune responses can be made against self constituents—such as, thyroglobulin in autoimmune thyroiditis; red cell antigens in autoimmune haemolytic anaemia; nuclear antigens in systemic lupus erythematosus; and even to part of the immunoglobulin molecule in rheumatoid arthritis (Ch. 9)

4. Laboratory assays
The knowledge that haptens can be made immunogenic by

combining them with carrier molecules has enabled an immune response to be generated to a large variety of clinically important substances, so that laboratory assays can be used to measure the substance. For example, assays for small polypeptide hormones and a variety of drugs (see *Radioimmunoassays* Ch. 10)

5. Protective immune responses

Antigens from microorganisms are used to induce a protective immune response against infection (Ch. 5). The important component of the immune response is that directed at surface antigens of the microorganism, particularly those involved in enabling the microorganism to attach to its target cell. Secreted molecules, such as microbial toxins, also induce a protective immune response

6. Route, dose, adjuvants

The route of administration of an antigen and its dose determine the strength of the immune response. Particulate antigens (e.g. bacteria) are immunogenic in a broad range of doses by various routes (e.g. subcutaneous or intravenous). Soluble antigens (e.g. serum proteins) often have to be combined with a helper substance called an *adjuvant* to induce an immune response. Adjuvants form a depot of antigen and allow its slow release.

7. Blood group antigens

These are clinically very important and much is known of their chemical structure and antigenic determinants. The ABO system includes four different blood groups A.B.O. and AB. Individuals do not develop immunity to their own blood group antigens but do make an immune response against other blood group antigens. This is thought to be due to immunisation by similar antigens present in gut bacteria. The ABO antigens are complex oligosaccharides located on the surface of the red blood cells and in a proportion of people—approximately 75%—in their tissue fluids and secretions. The immunodominant sugar in the A antigen is N-acetyl galactosamine; in the B antigen it is galactose; and in the H antigen, i.e. the one carried on group O cells, fucose is the dominant sugar

8. Vaccines

Recent advances in molecular biology have enabled the synthesis *in vitro* (using recombinant DNA technology) of several clinically important substances, including antigens of Hepatitis B virus for use as a vaccine. Many other such vaccines will be developed over the next few years

ESSENTIAL FEATURES

The essential features of the interaction of antigens with the cells of the immune system (see chapter on Antibodies for a more detailed description):

1. Inducer cells and T-lymphocytes
Most antigens entering the tissues interact first with *inducer cells*—macrophages, dendritic cells, Langerhans cells—and are presented to T-lymphocytes for initiation of immunity

2. The macrophages
These play a particularly important role as scavenger cells in taking up foreign antigen and degrading it by the lysosomal enzymes of its granules. Some antigen is disposed of and the remainder is expressed on the surface of the macrophage in combination with membrane receptors

3. T-helper cells
Antigen on the surface of inducer cells is recognised by a subclass of T-lymphocytes called T-helper cells and results in the release of mediatiors by T helper cells

4. Cellular and humoral immunity
A complex series of events is initiated that stimulates other lymphocytes to produce cellular immunity and humoral immunity. This includes T-lymphocytes called *cytotoxic T-lymphocytes* that take part in cellular immunity and B-lymphocytes that produce antibody. Macrophages are also activated to help the cellular immune response

5. Regulation
The response is internally regulated by feedback regulation due to antibodies and T suppressor cells but also by hormone-like factors called cytokines produced by cells within the immune system. Other forms of hormone control take place; e.g. thyroid and growth hormones enhance and glucocorticoids decrease the response. Pituitary peptides such as endorphins and corticotrophin have immunosuppressive effects and recent evidence suggests that neuroendocrine peptides are also produced by cells of the immune system, indicating possible reciprocal communication between the neuroendocrine and immune systems. Further understanding of these interrelationships are likely to lead to a better understanding of stress-related depression of immune reactivity and possibly new therapeutic approaches.

2. Tissues and cells of the immune system

TISSUES

Primary lymphoid tissues
1. *Bone Marrow* in which cells of immune system arise from stem cells
2. *Fetal liver* makes an important contribution to the origin of B-lymphocytes
3. *Thymus gland* in which T-lymphocytes derived from bone marrow stem cells migrate and differentiate. Here they gain their main functional activities. Their differentiation can be followed by loss of some and the appearance of new surface markers in their membranes

Secondary lymphoid tissues
1. *Lymph glands*, where differentiated T and B-lymphocytes migrate and occupy distinct sites in the organ, paracortex and cortex respectively. Macrophages and dendritic cells are present to trap antigens entering the glands during the passage of the lymph from afferent to efferent lymphatics
2. *Spleen*, where T and B lymphocytes are present in the white pulp around the central arteriole. The spleen also plays a role in haemopoiesis
3. Collections of non-encapsulated lymphoid cells are found in various organs, especially associated with mucous membranes of the respiratory and gastrointestinal tract e.g. tonsils and Peyers patches. These aggregates of cells are termed mucosal associated lymphoid tissue (MALT).
4. *Blood and lymph*, where B and T lymphocytes circulate—passing continuously in and out of the system and through the lymphoid organs. This is called *lymphocyte recirculation* (Fig. 2.1)

Notes
1. The structure and cells of the lymph nodes and spleen allow them to act as *filters* of the blood and lymph. Antigens are trapped in the deep cortex of lymph nodes by *inducer cells*—macrophages and specialised cells called dendritic cells (or sometimes

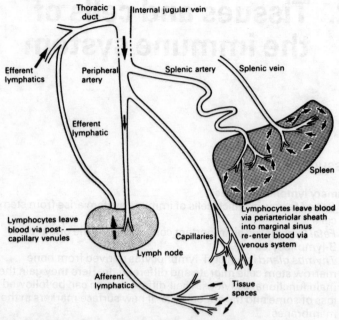

Fig. 2.1 Schematic view of main pathways of lymphocyte circulation

interdigitating cells). The skin contains macrophage-like cells
called *Langerhans cells* that also interact with antigen and
migrate via the lymph to the paracortex to interact with
lymphocytes

2. Once antibodies have been formed the antigens can then be
trapped even more effectively by complexes of antibody and
antigen attaching to receptors for immunoglobulin on the
macrophages. *Immunological memory* then develops

3. Unique blood vessels are present in the lymph nodes—the *post
capillary venules,* their specialised endothelial lining allows the
passage of the circulating lymphocytes

4. During an immune response lymph nodes enlarge—
lymphadenopathy. This is due to trapping of circulating
lymphocytes (possibly due to mediators produced by
macrophages—e.g. prostaglandins) and proliferation of cells *in
situ*

5. *Primary lymphoid follicles* in the cortex of lymph nodes become
germinal centres or secondary lymphoid follicles when
B-lymphocytes respond to the presence of antigen in both lymph
nodes and spleen (white pulp)

6. *T-lymphocytes* proliferate during an immune response in the
paracortical area of lymph nodes and the white pulp of the spleen

7. Collections of lymphoid cells can gather at sites of inflammation and form an *inflammatory granuloma* (e.g. at the site of a tuberculosis infection). The T and B lymphocytes in the granuloma can contribute to humoral and cellular immunity

Lymphocyte recirculation-functions (Fig. 2.1)
1. Allows access of lymphocytes to body tissues and organs to respond to any invading foreign antigen
2. Allows recruitment of lymphocytes to an inflammatory site and thus enables the initiation of immune response
3. Allows replenishment of lymphoid organs damaged by trauma, infection or X-rays

THE CELLS OF THE IMMUNE SYSTEM

The main cells of the immune system are *macrophages*, *T-lymphocytes* of various subclasses and *B-lymphocytes* (see above—for other inducer cells).
Polymorphonuclear leucocytes (neutrophils) are involved in non-specific innate immunity rather than the acquired immune response. *Eosinophils* are involved in allergic reactions and possibly in immunity to helminths and *basophils* release histamine and other mediators in allergic reactions.

Their origin
Figure 2.2 shows the origin of these cell types from the bone marrow stem cells and indicates the factors that regulate production and differentiation. Hormone-like factors are produced in lymphoid tissues and bring about differentiation. These tissues are called *haemopoiesis inducing microenvironments (HIMS)*.

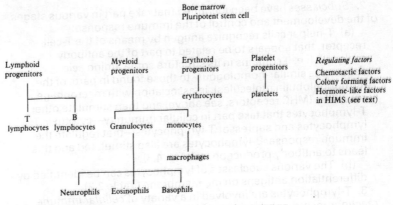

Fig. 2.2 Simplified scheme of haemopoiesis and regulation

Macrophages

1. Derived from bone marrow stem cells and make up the mononuclear phagocyte system.

2. Play an important role by phagocytosing microorganisms, then digesting them and presenting their antigenic components to the lymphocytes for induction of immunity. In the primary immune response (see below) dendritic cells are believed to play the predominant role in induction of the response

3. A wide range of membrane receptors enable macrophages to recognise foreign antigens, antigens coated with antibody and serum complement components (Ch. 5). Specific receptors of the major histocompatibility complex-MHC (coded for by Chromosome 6 in man and Chromosome 17 in the mouse, see Fig. 4.1) combine with antigen and the complex is recognised by helper T-lymphocytes. This leads to triggering of the immune response

4. Macrophages have a wide range of other activities including the production of mediators (termed monokines) that influence: T-lymphocytes (interleukin-1); bone marrow stem cells so that fresh supplies of macrophages are generated; prostaglandins which play an important role in inflammation; and many other mediators with effects on tumour cell growth, lipid metabolism and tissue regeneration (Table 2.1)

5. Macrophages have an essential role in cellular immunity because they provide immunity to a range of intracellular microorganisms—such as tubercle bacilli and viruses.

6. Acting in conjunction with antibodies macrophages can kill infected cells and tumour cells. This activity is called *antibody dependent cell mediated cytotoxicity (ADCC)*

T-lymphocytes

1. *Derived* from bone marrow stem cells and *differentiated* within the thymus gland

2. *Subclasses* have been identified that take part in various stages of the development and control of the immune response:

(a) T-helper cells recognize antigen by means of the T-cell receptor, that appears to be related to part of the antibody molecule (i.e. it contains in its structure some amino acid sequences similar-homologous- to those found in parts of the immunoglobulin molecules), in association with macrophage receptors (MHC receptors, see above) and then stimulate other T-lymphocytes that take part in cellular immunity—cytotoxic T lymphocytes and supressor T-lymphocytes—that regulate the immune response. B-lymphocytes are also stimulated and this leads to antibody production (see Fig. 4.3)

(b) The various subclasses of lymphocytes can be identified by differentiation antigens on the membrane (Table 2.2)

3. T-lymphocytes are involved in a variety of *cellular immune reactions* including contact sensitivity in the skin to simple

Table 2.1 Lymphokines and monokines

Factor	Source	Functions
Mitogenic factor Blastogenic factor Lymphocyte transformation factor	lymphocytes	Recruitment of additional lymphocytes Initiating lymphocyte proliferation to enhance response
Chemotactic factors	lymphocytes	Part of inflammatory response to attract macrophages and neutrophils to site of immune response
Interferons	lymphocytes and macrophages	Provides protection against viral replication; activates macrophages and Natural Killer cells
Interleukin-1	macrophages	Stimulates T-helper cells and thymocytes to proliferate and produce mature T-cells that release their own growth promoting factors; stimulates liver cells to produce 'acute phase proteins' and induces fever
Interleukin-2	lymphocytes	Promotes proliferation of T-helper and cytotoxic cells
Interleukin-3	lymphocytes	Proliferation of bone marrow precursor cells
B cell growth and differentiation factors (BCGF, BCDF)	lymphocytes	Promotes (along with other factors) B cell differentiation towards antibody production
Lymphotoxin	lymphocytes	A protein that causes destruction of tumours cells in vitro
Macrophage inhibition factor Macrophage aggregation factor	lymphocytes	Retains macrophages at site of inflammatory response
Macrophage activating factor	lymphocytes	Triggers microbicidal and tumoricidal activity in macrophages

Table 2.2 Mature T-cell differentiation markers

	Mouse		Human	
	Ly1	Ly2	T4	T8
Helper	+	−	+	−
Suppressor	−	+	−	+
Cytolytic	−	+	−	+

chemicals, delayed hypersensitivity reactions (Ch. 8) to certain types of antigen, for example: tuberculin (a sterile extract of complex protein constituents of the tubercle bacillus) response in the skin—Mantoux test described in chapter 10; and in transplantation immunity to graft antigens (Ch. 1)

4. T-lymphocyte *activity* can be assessed by testing their ability to proliferate in the presence of certain extracts of plants—plant mitogens, e.g. *phytohaemagluttinin PHA.*

5. T-lymphocytes produce a variety of mediators called *lymphokines* that can activate macrophages and other T-lymphocytes (Table 2.1)

6. The expression of lymphocyte surface structures can be modified by a recently developed process called *transfection,* in which genetic information for the surface structure is artificially introduced into the lymphocyte. The procedure enables the study of the function of the introduced structure. The transfected genes can be manipulated before introduction to see the effect that changes in sequence have on the expression and function of the gene products

B-lymphocytes

1. *Derived* like other cells of the immune system from bone marrow stem cells

2. The B-cell *recognizes* antigen by means of antibody molecules in its cell membrane that act as receptors

3. A B-cell can essentially make *antibody of only one specificity,* so that many B cells are required to recognize the wide range of antigens in the environment—approximately 10^7

4. The mature B-cell is not an antibody secreting cell but can readily *differentiate* on antigenic stimulation *to the plasma cell* that synthesizes and secretes antibody. The plasma cell contains much endoplasmic reticulum that enables rapid bulk protein synthesis but they do not divide. They live only two or three days

5. *Stimulation* of B-cells usually requires the co-operation of T cells (as noted above) and requires compatibility at the level of the MHC (as with the macrophage) and are probably mainly active in secondary responses (i.e. after clonal expansion and development of immunological memory)

6. Certain antigens appear to be able to *stimulate* B-cells directly—T-independent antigens, e.g. large molecules with repeating antigenic determinants

7. The *class of antibody* (Ch. 3) expressed on a B-cell *changes* following antigenic stimulation—genetic switch—the part of the antibody molecule that combines with the specific antigen remains unchanged but other parts of the molecule are changed to those of another class of antibody. This results in generation of antibody molecules with a variety of useful functional activities (Ch. 3)

CLINICAL CONSIDERATIONS

Immunosuppressive drugs
Immunosuppressive drugs—given, for example, in the control of transplant rejection—can interfere with the ability of the immune system to combat infection. Such drugs are non-selective in their action and interfere not only with lymphocytes rejecting a graft but also with those that would respond to infective agents. A new drug *Cyclosporin A* appears to be more selective in its actions

Viruses
Certain viruses attack cells of the immune system. For example: macrophages can be attacked by *Herpes simplex* virus and by arboviruses; B-lymphocytes by Epstein Barr virus; and the T-lymphocytes by HTLV 3 (or lymphadenopathy associated virus) of AIDS. This leads to interference with normal functioning of the immune system—often shown up by changes in the ratio of helper T-lymphocytes to supressor T-lymphocytes as in AIDS; or changes in the B-lymphocytes as in infectious mononucleosis

Adjuvants
Products of certain microorganisms—for example, bacterial endotoxin of Gram-negative bacteria and cell wall constituents of mycobacteria—can act as adjuvants (see above) and thus enhance the immune response. Such materials can be used clinically in combined vaccines, e.g. the triple vaccine containing pertussis antigens, which act as adjuvants (Ch. 6)

Tumours
Tumours of the immune system either affecting the lymphoid cells directly as in leukaemias, or indirectly as metastasis from other tumours affect the normal functioning of the system. Tumours of B-lymphocytes are characterized by the presence of abnormal protein bands on electrophoresis—e.g. myelomas

Autoimmune diseases
In autoimmune diseases disturbances in regulation of the immune response can be found. They may take the form of changes in the ratio of T and B lymphocytes. It is not yet known if these effects are brought about by infectious agents, such as viruses, or whether there are genetically determined defects within the immune cell population

Immune deficiences
Primary Immune deficiency states can affect any of the cells of the lymphoid cell population (Ch. 7) with predictable consequences on the ability of the patient to mount an immune response

Modification of immune response
As lymphokines and monokines (e.g. Interleukins and interferons) become available by means of recent advances in DNA technology it should become possible to modify the immune response. For example—by suppressing it, as might be advantageous in autoimmunity; or enhancing it, when immunosupression has occured, e.g. in AIDS

Parasitic infections
Non-specific suppression is a feature of parasite infections (worms, protozoa) and affects both humoral and cell-mediated immunity. In schistosomiasis, for example, T helper cells are suppressed. Trypanosomes and other parasites cause polyclonal activation of B lymphocytes leading to depletion of antigen reactive B cells. Thus individuals with parasitic infections are particularly susceptible to bacterial and viral infections

Bacterial infections
Mycobacterium leprae affects immune function by altering lymphocyte recirculation due to trapping of lymphocytes in granuloma. The bacteria also affect T cell areas of lymph nodes (paracortex) and appear to activate T suppressor cells. Patients with syphilis have an immunosuppressive factor in their serum. Bacterial lipopolysaccharide can both suppress and enhance the immune response e.g. by effects on macrophages and on T cells. Peptidoglycans from Gram-positive bacteria stimulates the release of interleukin-1 from monocytes leading to pyrogenic effects

3. Antibodies or immunoglobulins

GENERAL FEATURES

1. Gamma-globulin proteins with antibody activity are referred to as *immunoglobulins*
2. All immunoglobulin molecules have a *common structure* of four polypeptide chains—two large, or heavy chains, and two small, or light chains (Fig 3.1)
3. There are *five classes* of human immunoglobulin—IgG, IgM, IgA, IgE and IgD
4. The differences between the classes depends upon differences in their heavy chains. The differences are called *isotypes*
5. IgG *heavy chains* are designated gamma (γ) chains, IgM are mu (μ) chains, IgA are alpha (α) chains, IgE are epsilon (ϵ) chains and IgD are delta (δ) chains
6. There are only two types of *light chain* kappa (κ) and lambda (λ.)
7. In human IgG, approximately 65% of the molecules have two kappa light chains and 35% have two lambda chains associated with the heavy chains
8. Human IgM and IgA are known to have a similar arrangement but this has not yet been established for the other classes
9. The basic immunoglobulin structure consists of *12 domains*, each made up of approximately 110 amino-acids. Each heavy chain being made up of four such domains and each light chain of two of these domains. IgE has an additional domain (p. 20)
10. The ability of an antibody molecule to combine with antigen depends upon a region called the *antigen binding site* or Fab. Here the particular sequence of amino-acids provides a configuration complementary to that of the antigen
11. These sequences differ for antibodies of different specificities (variable sequences) and are determined by what are termed variable or *V-genes* (see below). The *variable domains* of the light and heavy chains (one in each chain) are called VL and VH. Each of these regions contains areas where the amino-acid sequences appear to vary more than in other areas. These are called *hypervariable* regions and contribute to the antigen binding site

15

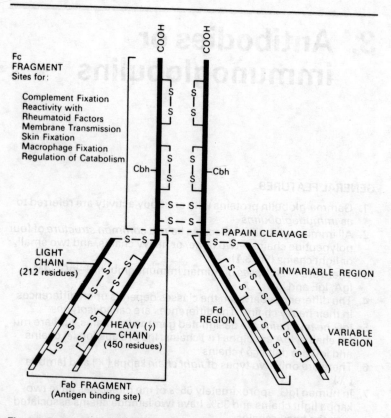

Fig. 3.1 Diagrammatic view of structural arrangements of polypeptide chains of immunoglobulin molecule. The chains are held together by three disulphide bonds. Pepsin splits the molecule, leaving an Fc fragment (crystallizable) and Fd parts of the heavy chains with attached light chains—the whole making Fab (or antigen binding) fragments. The N terminal ends of the light and heavy chains have variable sequences of amino-acids as shown by the broken line. There are also a number of intra-chain disulphide bonds which influence the shape of individual chains. The carbohydrate (Cbh) groups may be concerned with the catabolism of the molecule

12. The remainder of the antibody molecule consists of so called constant sequences being very similar one to the other. These constant regions are present in each immunoglobulin class, both in light and heavy chains—CL and CH. The *constant domains* determine certain biological activities of the molecule (see Table 3.1).

Table 3.1 Immunoglobulin classes

Immunoglobulin class	Molecular characteristics	Approximate serum concentration mg/dl	Molecular weight Daltons	Half life days	Heavy chain	Biological activities
IgG	monomer	1100	150 000	21	gamma	Toxin neutralization Agglutination Opsonins Bacteriolytic (with complement) Ag/Ab complexes can mediate tissue injury IgG is a late antibody
IgM	monomeric on B cells pentamer in serum with J chain	100	900 000	5	mµ	IgM is an early antibody and antigen receptor on B lymphocytes
IgA	monomer and dimer with J chain and secretory piece	250	150 000–350 000	6	alpha	Surface protection Toxin neutralization
IgD	monomer	3	180 000	3	delta	Antigen receptor on B-lymphocytes
IgE	monomer	0.1	190 000	2	epsilon	Antibody involved in allergic Type 1 hypersensitivity reactions. Immunity in worm infections Ag interacting with mast cell IgE may trigger mediator release causing increased capillary permeability, so that Ab containing plasma and phagocytes can reach invading microorganism or toxin

Immunoglobulin G—IgG

1. This is the major immunoglobulin component of serum, approximately 75% of the total
2. The molecular weight of the molecule is 150 000, with a sedimentation coefficient of 7S.
3. Each IgG molecule is made up of two kappa or lambda light chains and two gamma heavy chains (Fig 3.1).
4. Each molecule has two binding sites for antigen (Fab region) coded for by the variable genes (see above)
5. Genetically determined *subgroups* of Immunoglobulin exist called *allotypes* (comparable to blood groups). Three main subgroups have been defined (Gm, Am and Km) and each can be further subdivided. The Am allotype is found in a subclass of IgA antibodies. Gm determinants are in the gamma chains of IgG only and Km are in the kappa light chains of each immunoglobulin class
6. Four *subclasses* of IgG have been found based on differences in amino—acid sequences in the heavy chains. These differences act as antigenic determinants (Ch. 1) and enable antisera to be prepared against the subclasses. The subclasses are called IgG1, IgG2, IgG3 and IgG4 (Fig. 3.2) and vary slightly in their functions (see below)
7. A degree of subclass restriction has been observed in the antibody response to certain types of antigen, e.g. IgG2 to certain carbohydrate antigens. This can be important as the functional activities of the subclasses differs. For example, IgG3 binds complement components much more effectively than IgG1 and IgG4 fails to bind complement at all IgG2 and IgG4 are unable to bind to Ig receptors (Fc receptors, see p. 24) on monocytes
8. The Fab component of the Immunoglobulin molecule because of differences in amino—acid sequences between antibodies of differing specificity are themselves able to act as antigens. The antigenic determinants are called *idiotypic determinants*

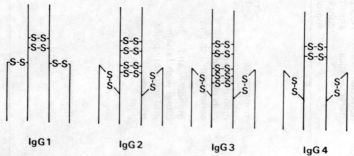

IgG 1   IgG 2   IgG 3   IgG 4

Fig. 3.2 IgG subclasses showing variable arrangements of the disulphide bonds

Immunoglobulin M—IgM

1. IgM has a molecular weight of about 900 000 Daltons. Each molecule of IgM consists of five identical subunits of about 180 000 daltons
2. Each subunit consists of two kappa or lambda light chains and two mu (μ) heavy chains
3. The molecule takes the shape of a circular pentamer joined by disulphide bonds (Fig. 3.3). An additional chain is present, called the J or joining chain, holding the molecule into its pentameric shape. This chain is found also in IgA dimers (see below)
4. Because of its high molecular weight IgM is normally restricted to the blood rather than the tissue fluids (see below)

Immunoglobulin A—IgA

1. Monomeric IgA (it can exist in polymeric forms) has a molecular weight of 150 000 daltons and has the same numbers of

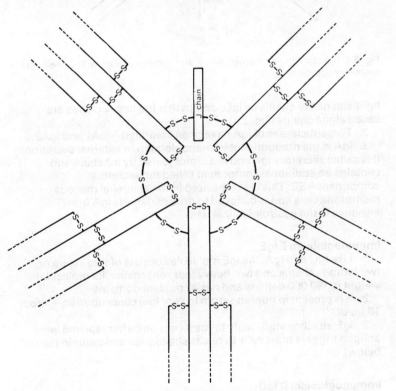

Fig. 3.3 IgM structure showing five subunits and multiple combining sites

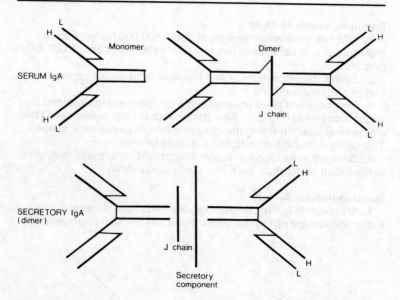

Fig. 3.4 IgA showing monomer, dimer and secretory form, with J chain and secretory component

light and heavy chains as IgG, except that the heavy chains are called alpha chains (Fig. 3.4)

2. Two subclasses of IgA have been identified—IgA1 and IgA2

3. IgA is the predominant immunoglobulin of external secretions. It is called secretory IgA and is a dimer joined by a J chain and contains an additional component called the secretory component—SC. This is synthesized in the epithelial mucous membrane cells and is believed to protect dimeric IgA from enzymes in the gastrointestinal tract

Immunoglobulin E IgE

1. Like IgG and IgA, the IgE molecule consists of two kappa or two lambda chains and two heavy (epsilon) chains. Its molecular weight is 190 000 daltons and has 4 constant domains

2. It is present in human serum in very low concentration—about $10 \ \mu g/dl^{-1}$

3. IgE attaches vigorously to mast cells and after reacting with antigen triggers mast cells to release histamine and heparin (see below)

Immunoglobulin D IgD

1. IgD is a minor component of serum immunoglobulins—3 to 50 μg per ml of serum.

2. The molecule is also present on the membrane of B-lymphocytes along with monomeric IgM and is believed to play a role in the differentiation of the B cell

3. The biological activities of the molecule are largely unknown but occasionally antibody activity has been associated with IgD—for example, against penicillin, diptheria toxin and certain autoantibodies (such as those against cell nuclei) have been found to be of this class

4. IgD does not cross the placenta and is absent from cord serum

MOLECULAR GENETICS OF IMMUNOGLOBULIN SYNTHESIS

1. The genes for the light (kappa and lambda) and heavy chains are carried on different chromosomes (2,22 and 14 in man) and are divided up into *coding exons* and *non-coding (silent) introns* like the genes for other macromolecules. Both exons and introns are transcribed into mRNA but the intron segments are excised and the molecule respliced before translation into protein takes place

2. In the mouse (for which most detail is known) there are three sets of genes for the kappa light chain V, J and C genes— (chromosome 6). The lambda gene (chromosome 16) consists of two pairs of V genes and three pairs of J and C genes

3. The heavy chain gene is made up of four gene segments V,D,J, and C in a cluster of between one and two hundred different segments each of about 295 base pairs (chromosome 12)

4. Variability in amino-acid sequence for antibodies of different specificity is created by rearrangements of the different gene segments coding for the variable region of the molecule. V and J segments for the light chains and V,D and J segments for the heavy chains

5. The random arrangements that arise generate enormous diversity amongst the immunoglobulin population—between 10^6 and 10^7 different specificities

6. Two other sources of diversity exist:
    (a) There is a lack of precision of the DNA splicing machinery that fuses V, D and J segments so that the site of the junction varies by several base pairs
    (b) Cloning and sequencing of immunoglobulin genes showed that somatic mutation takes place in the variable domains and in the immediately adjacent regions but not in the constant domains. Estimates of the mutation rate indicate that one change in the V regions occurs for every three to 30 cell divisions. This rate is higher than that normally found in eukaryotic cells

7. The effect of these processes is initially to provide a population of cells that carry a wide range of specificities for antigen. The mutational mechanism occurs during proliferation of B cell clones that have been selected by antigen resulting in antibody that is 'fine tuned' to match the inducing antigen

CLINICAL CONSIDERATIONS

Myeloma proteins
(a) Myeloma proteins are produced by tumours of plasma cells in the bone marrow. These tumours invade the bones. The cells are a clone of identical immunoglobulin secreting cells. The immunoglobulin can be of any class.
(b) Myeloma proteins are found in the serum (detected electrophoretically) and in the urine where they are called Bence-Jones proteins and are made up of light chains recognizable by their ability to coagulate at 60^0 C and redissolve at 80^0 C.

Waldenstroms macrogloblinaemia
In Waldenstroms macrogloblinaemia IgM is produced (here the tumour does not invade the bone)

Monoclonal antibodies
Clones of antibody forming cells can now be grown *in vitro* by fusing an antibody producing B-cell with a myeloma cell to produce a hybrid myeloma cell called a *hybridoma*. Hybridomas are used to produce *monoclonal antibodies*.

STEPS IN PREPARATION OF MONOCLONAL ANTIBODY

Immunization. Mouse (or rat) immunized with antigen—primary then booster immunization

Fusion. Spleen cells taken from immunized mouse and fused with a myeloma cell (a mutant not producing antibody) using polyethylene glycol

Selection of hybridoma. Myeloma cells used lack an enzyme hypoxanthine phosphoribosyl transferase so cannot grow in a medium *containing hypoxanthine, aminopterin and thymidine (HAT medium).* Spleen cells cannot grow because they are not a continuous cell line. Hybridoma cells can grow as they have the transferase derived from the spleen cells and the capacity of the myeloma to grow in continuous culture

Screening. Clones are screened for antibody production (may represent about 10% of the cells)

Propagation. Positive clones are propagated from single cell preparations and should produce 10 to 100 μg/ml of specific antibody. They can be grown in mouse peritoneal cavity and the ascitic fluid containing the antibody can be collected

Storage. The antibody rich fluid can be freeze dried or hybridoma cells can be stored at −70°C and used as stock cultures

CLINICAL APPLICATIONS

1. Monoclonal antibodies have a wide range of clinical applications—for example, as *laboratory reagents* in the diagnosis of infection and assays of peptide hormones, or the identification of surface markers on cells in biopsy material. They are being used *experimentally* to: deliver drugs to particular tissue sites; in the diagnosis and treatment of tumours; and in fertility control in animals.

2. Monoclonal antibodies are being increasingly used in *affinity chromatography* to isolate and purify many molecules of clinical importance, including material for *vaccines* and *interferon*.

3. The possibility of producing large quantities of monoclonal antibody against antigens of microorganisms *in vitro* is likely to lead to their use in *passive immunization* (injection of antibody in contrast to antigen) to control infections—due for example to *Streptococcus pneumoniae* or other parasites that remain accessible to antibody during infection.

4. Monoclonal antibodies are being used as probes to screen recombinant DNA libraries derived from bacteria to identify antigens e.g. *Mycobacterium tuberculosis* and *Mycobacterium leprae*. The information gained should be useful not only for taxonomic studies but also for the identification of gene products that could be used in diagnosis or for the production of vaccines.

4. The acquired immune response

STEPS IN GENERATION OF ANTIBODY

Antibody production
Antibody production requires four cell types: *Macrophages* and other *inducer cells* (dendritic cells of the lymph nodes and spleen and B lymphocytes see below). *Helper* and *suppressor T lymphocytes* and *B lymphocytes*

Mediator release
Macrophages (and other inducer cells) and helper T-lymphocytes act together and mediators are released that trigger the activities of the other cell types

Antigen recognition
Macrophages (and other inducer cells) first recognize antigen by means of receptors on their plasma membrane—*Fc receptors*, if the antigen is combined with antibody produced on an earlier occasion; or other receptors coded for by the *Major histocompatibility* (MHC) gene complex that are essential for the initiation of the cellular events that lead to an immune response

Antigen processing
The antigen is taken into the inducer cell broken down by its lysosomal enzymes and some of the material is re-expressed on the plasma membrane in association with MHC antigens called Class 2 antigens—it is uncertain at present, if antigen processing is required for all antigens; because in some instances, antigens appear to be presented without prior degradation and reexpression.

Helper T-lymphocytes
(a) Helper T-lymphocytes recognize the antigen in association with the inducer cell membrane receptors. Receptors containing regions homologous but not identical to part of the immunoglobulin variable and constant regions are present on the T-cell and carry out the above *recognition function*. The T-cell receptor is a heterodimer consisting of an alpha and beta chain coded for on different

chromosomes (14 and 6 respectively in the mouse and 14 and 7 in man). Another chain called gamma is also part of the structure of the receptor, but its role is uncertain at present. T-cell clones are now available that enable the detailed study of T-cell function.

(b) The helper T-lymphocyte is stimulated by a *mediator* produced by macrophages called *Interleukin-1* or *IL-1*.

(c) The helper T-lymphocyte itself produces another *mediator* called *Interleukin-2* (IL-2) that binds to a receptor on helper T-lymphocytes induced by IL-1 (as well as on T-lymphocytes involved in cell mediated immunity, cytotoxic T-lymphocytes. Tc and T-cells involved in delayed hypersensitivity Tdh—see below) and promotes the activity of these cells

(d) Another *mediator* called *Interleukin-3* (IL-3) is produced by the T-lymphocytes and plays a role in stimulating bone marrow stem cells to produce fresh supplies of granulocytes

B-cells
(a) B-cells carry immunoglobulin molecules in their membrane that act as receptors for the antigen and can recognize it in association with T-cells—except for T-independent antigens, which are molecules with repeating antigenic determinants that can stimulate B-cells directly

(b) In addition, T-cells produce factors that promote B-cell activity called *T replacing factor* (TRF) and *B-cell growth factor* (BCGF)

The B-cell thus triggered differentiates to an *antibody producing plasma cell*

(c) B-cells can *interact directly with T-helper cells* without the intervention of macrophages but here too, as with macrophages, there is genetic restriction by Class 2 antigens

Suppressor T-cells
Suppressor T-cells appear to act on helper T-cells by producing *antigen specific suppressor factors* that suppress the immune response to the antigen

CLONAL SELECTION THEORY OF BURNET

1. B-cells express a surface immunoglobulin that, as noted above, acts as an *antigen binding receptor*

2. *Contact* with antigen leads to division and antibody production. All the cells resulting from this division produce antibody of the same specificity—i.e. with the same heavy and light chain variable region in the Fab section. These cells are called *a clone* or family.

3. Some of the clone become memory cells that express the same Ig receptor and can respond rapidly to later contact with the same antigen that originally induced their formation. This process is called *clonal expansion*.

4. The selection theory suggests that during *fetal development* any clone that reacts with self-antigens is eliminated and this is supported by experimental evidence showing that clones that can react with foreign antigens can also be eliminated provided the antigen is given very early in life. This phenomenon is called *immune tolerance*—see Chapter 9 for a detailed discussion of self-tolerance.

5. The theory is called a *selection theory* because the role of antigen is to *select* the particular B-cell carrying a receptor of appropriate specificity that is able to recognize the antigen.

HISTOCOMPATIBILITY ANTIGENS AND THE IMMUNE RESPONSE

1. Coded for by the major histocompatibility gene complex (MHC) on chromosome 6 in man and 17 in the mouse
2. The glycoprotein gene products are expressed on the surface of various cells
3. Three classes of MHC gene products are important in immunity:
   Class 1 antigens determine graft rejection and also associate with viral antigens enabling the infected cell to be recognized by cytotoxic T-cells.
   Class 2 antigens act as receptors for the presentation of antigen to helper T-cells. These antigens are sometimes referred to as immune response or IR gene products.
   Class 3 antigens are involved in the production of components of the complement system (see p. 35).
4. Class 1 antigens are expressed on most nucleated cell—this enables tissue cells infected with a virus to be recognized by cytotoxic T-cells
5. Class 2 antigens are found on macrophages, dendritic cells of the lymph nodes and spleen. Langerhans cells in the skin, B lymphocytes, activated T lymphocytes, vascular endothelium and some epithelial cells
6. Lymphokines can promote and increase the expression of Class 2 antigens on various cell types
7. Figure 4.1 shows the arrangement of the genes in the MHC of mouse and man
8. Class 1 and 2 antigens are glycoproteins made up of two chains with an extracellular, a hydrophobic transmembrane and a cytoplasmic segment
9. Class 1 antigens consist of a heavy chain of 45 000 Daltons and a light chain of 12 000 Daltons (Beta-2 microglobulin) and Class 2 antigens are heterodimers of an alpha and a beta chain of 34 000 and 28 000 Daltons respectively (Fig. 4.2)

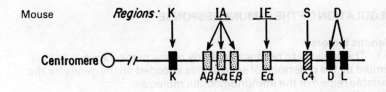

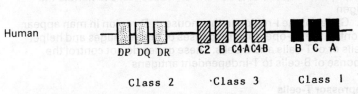

Class 2   ·Class 3   Class 1

Fig. 4.1 Simplified view of the major histocompatibility gene complex. Class 1 genes are shown as filled boxes. Class 2 as stippled boxes and Class 3 are shown as cross-hatched boxes. Mouse Class 2 genes IA and IE code for the alpha and beta chains of the Class 2 glycoproteins. There are three genes in the human D region and a number of Class 3 genes that code for components of the complement system

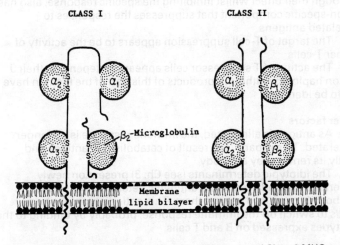

Fig. 4.2 Simplified diagram of the structure of Class 1 and Class 2 MHC gene products. There are at least six alpha and eight beta chain genes in the human Class 2 region. DR-alpha in non-polymorphic, DQ-alpha is highly polymorphic and DP-alpha is intermediate. DP-beta is less polymorphic than DR-beta or DQ-beta

REGULATION OF THE IMMUNE RESPONSE

Genetic factors
1. The capacity to produce antibody of any particular specificity is limited by the repertoire of specificities encoded on the genes for the variable region of the immunoglobulin molecule
2. Mice have been selectively bred that have the ability to respond well or poorly to particular antigens. The genes that control this ability appear to control the ability of inducer cells to handle the antigen
3. Genes of the I-region in the mouse or D-region in man appear to control the co-operative responses of macrophages and helper T-cells or of T-cells and B-cells. These genes do not control the response of B-cells to T-independent antigens

Suppressor T-cells
1. A variety of factors that lead to the induction of suppressor T-cell activity have been identified:
   (a) Very low or high doses of antigen
   (b) Repeated doses of antigen, e.g. in chronic infective states
   (c) Long persistence of antigen, e.g. if injected intravenously—particularly if not taken up readily by phagocytes
2. The generation of suppressor T-cells is highly specific—although their effect whilst inhibiting the specific response, also has a non-specific component that suppresses the responses to unrelated antigens
3. The target of T-cell suppression appears to be the activity of helper T-cells
4. The action of T suppressor cells appears to depend on their J region haplotype although products of this part of the I region have yet to be identified

Other factors
1. As antigen is eliminated, the immune response is no longer generated. This is partly the result of catabolism of antigen and partly its removal by antibody
2. The idiotypic determinants (see Ch. 3) present on newly generated antibody can act as antigenic determinants, so that antibody is produced against them. This anti-idiotypic antibody tends to switch off the immune response, probably by binding to the idiotypes expressed on B and T cells

Primary and secondary responses
1. Following initial contact with antigen, the dendritic cells of the lymphoid tissues (and Langerhans cells of the skin) are the main inducers of T-lymphocyte activation. The processes outlined above occur rapidly but antibody does not appear in measurable quantity in the blood until nearly a week afterwards (Fig. 4.3). This called a

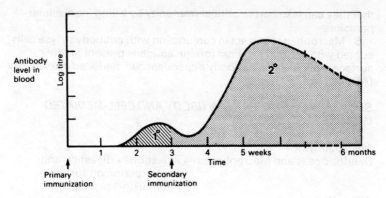

Fig. 4.3 The antibody response

primary immune response. Most of the antibody produced at this stage is of the IgM class.

2. IgG and other classes of antibody are then produced (genetic switch p. 13) but the overall response is poor and soon falls off.

3. Further contact with antigen—e.g. a second injection—leads to a very rapid and steeply rising appearance of antibody within a day or two. This is called a *secondary response* and involves memory cells (see above)

4. A secondary response can be from 10 to 50 times that of a primary response and is long lasting. Macrophages play an important role in processing and presenting antigen at this stage—they also remove excess antigen by enzymic degradation.

5. Most of the immunoglobulin produced in a secondary response is IgG or other classes—such as IgA, particularly if immunity is developed in the mucous membranes

Cellular or cell-mediated immunity

1. Cell-mediated or cellular immune responses are carried out by subclasses of *T-lymphocytes and by macrophages*

2. *Cytotoxic T-cells* can lyse cells that carry a foreign antigen on their surface, e.g. viral antigens, tumour antigens or cells of incompatible grafts. IL-2 is responsible for the generation of cytotoxic T cells

3. *Delayed hypersensitivity*. T-cells release mediators that bring about an inflammatory response involving attraction of macrophages, neutrophils and other lymphocytes to the site. The classical example of a delayed hypersensitivity response is the tuberculin reaction in the skin that follows the injection of tubercle bacilli or their products in a previously sensitised individual

4. T-lymphocytes produce a large variety of mediators called *lymphokines*, some of which attract and activate macrophages so

that they can take part in cellular immunity by killing intracellular parasites

5. Macrophages can act in conjunction with antibody to lyse cells coated with antibody against foreign antigens present on their surface. This is called *antibody dependent cell mediated cytotoxicity* (ADCC).

SUMMARY OF STAGES IN ANTIBODY AND CELL-MEDIATED IMMUNE RESPONSE

Main pathway
Dendritic cells and Macrophages → ingestion → digestion and
re-expression on surface.
Interleukin-1 production

Minor Pathway
B-lymphocytes → antigen bound to Ig receptors on those cells
expressing Ig specific for the antigen—which can,
in special circumstances, trigger B-cells directly

1. Antigen recognized on macrophages or B-lymphocytes in association with MHC Class 2 molecules by T-helper lymphocytes. This triggers Interleukin-2 production by T helper cells
2. Interleukin-1 from macrophages increases the number of receptors on T helper cells for Interleukin-2
3. Mitosis, production of B cell growth factors and clonal expression resulting in generation of effector T- and B-lymphocytes:
    (a) Cytotoxic T cells—T_c
    (b) Delayed hypersensitivity T-cell—T_{dh} that produce lymphokines
    (c) Suppressor T-cells—T_s regulate immune response
    (d) B-lymphocytes differentiate into plasma cells to produce immunoglobulins

CLINICAL CONSIDERATIONS

1. A secondary immune response can be induced by injecting antigen in conjunction with an adjuvant (p. 13)
2. The quality (avidity) of antibody increases late in an immune response as decreasing amounts of antigen are available to stimulate B-cells expressing immunoglobulin receptors best able to capture antigen
3. The humoral immune response is able to neutralize microbial toxins, clump and localize bacteria and other invading microorganisms described in chapter 6
4. The cell mediated immune response is active against virus infected cells, incompatible grafts and tumour cells (Ch. 6, 1, 9)
5. The various regulatory factors, like the interleukins, can be

produced *in vitro* by recombinant DNA technology and are likely
to play an increasing role as therapeutic agents
6. Clinical symptoms, such as fever, are brought about by IL-1
acting on the temperature control centre in the brain. Interferon
produced during immune responses to viruses is believed to be
responsible for 'flu like' symptoms
7. Acute phase substances—such a C reactive protein (CRP), that
are characteristic of inflammatory states—are induced by IL-1
acting on hepatocytes. Acute phase protein levels are assessed
in clinical practice as a guide to the progress of the inflammatory
state
8. Interference (e.g. by virus infection) in Ts cell activity is
suggested as an underlying cause of autoimmunity (Ch. 9)
9. Interference by HTLV 3 virus of AIDS with Th cells prevents
normal responses to opportunist pathogens
10. Tdh cells can be responsible for damaging inflammatory
responses—delayed hypersensitivity
11. Inducer cells, e.g. Langerhans cells in the skin can be affected by
ultra-violet irradiation and appear in mouse experiments to lead
to spread of Herpes simplex infection and may explain the
association of exposure to sunlight and herpes lesions in
humans
12. In immune deficiency states (Ch. 7) any of the cell populations,
particularly those in the minor pathway, can be affected with
predictable effects on the immune response

5. Inflammation and augmentation of the immune response

INFLAMMATION

1. Stimuli leading to an inflammatory response may be:
    Physical—damage to skin or other tissue or organ
    Chemical—noxious chemicals
    Microorganisms—toxins
    Immunological—hypersensitivity reactions
2. The inflammation can be acute (short lasting) or chronic (long lasting):
    Acute signs are redness, heat, swelling and pain
    Chronic often follows acute (sometimes after a very brief acute phase). The essential difference is that inflammation and repair occur simultaneously with persistent suppuration and ulceration, which often leads to fibrosis

Acute inflammation

Main features
1. Dilatation of blood vessels.
2. Increased vascular permeability.
3. Emigration of leucocytes along with inflammatory exudate.

Functions
1. Clot formation localizes foreign micro-organism and prevents loss of blood at the site of injury
2. Exudate contains antimicrobial agents such as antibody and complement
3. Exudate continually drained via lymphatics so that microorganism or toxin drained to lymph nodes and immune response initiated

Leucocytes in inflammation
1. *Polymorphonuclear granulocytes*—neutrophils and other granulocytes, eosinophils and basophils—are attracted to the site by a process called *chemotaxis*, which is mediated by complement

components and other pharmacological agents generated in inflammation:

(a) Neutrophils phagocytose and degrade microorganisms. They contain lysosomal granules with a variety of enzymes that play a major role in solubilising dead and damaged tissue or microorganisms.

(b) Eosinophils are found in inflammatory responses involving helminths and in allergic responses. They have granules containing enzymes that can degrade mediators of inflammation such as histamine

2. *Macrophages* are the other important cell type in inflammation, which:

(a) Predominate in later stages of inflammation

(b) Have a longer life span than neutrophils

(c) Can phagocytose and digest foreign material (cf. neutrophils)

(d) Produce a variety of pharmacolocical mediators of inflammation

(e) Have an important role in resolution of inflammation by removing dead cells and fibrin

(f) Play a very important role in the initiation of the immune response (Ch. 4)

Mechanisms of phagocytosis

1. Phagocytes (both neutrophils and macrophages) have *receptors* on their membrane that can recognize foreign agents, such as microorganisms:

(a) There are three main types of receptor:
— *Lectin receptors*—These bind bacteria by recognizing their cell wall sugars
— *Fc receptors*—which recognize bacteria or viruses coated with antibody
— *C3 receptors*—which recognize micro-organisms coated with complement components

Triggering of Fc and lectin receptors leads to activation of the phagocyte—respiratory burst and release of mediators

(b) Antibody or complement coated particles are referred to as **opsonised**

2. The phagocyte membrane folds around the particle and the particle is taken into the cytoplasm enclosed in a *phagocytic vesicle* or **phagosome**

3. The phagosome fuses with a lysosomal granule to form a **phagolysosome** and the contents of the lysosome degrade the ingested particle

4. In the case of the *macrophage* as already noted (Ch. 4) some of the *degraded material* is re-expressed on the membrane in association with MHC products and **initiates immunity**

Degradation and killing of microorganisms

Two main processes are involved:

(a) *Oxygen dependent system*—the peroxidase–myeloperoxidase halide system. Phagocytosis is followed by a respiratory burst involving the hexose monophosphate shunt. Leads to conversion of oxygen to superoxide anion, hydrogen peroxide, singlet oxygen and hydroxyl radicals that destroy micro-organisms. Myeloperoxidase generates free halide ions that have powerful antimicrobial activities.

(b) *Oxygen independent system* involves killing by: low pH, lysozyme, lactoferrin, leukin, phagocytin and a variety of hydrolytic enzymes that damage bacterial cell walls.

Pharmacological mediators of inflammation

There are two types of mediator—exogenous and endogenous:

(a) *Exogenous mediators* can be produced by micro-organisms and be directly responsible for increases in vascular permeability and chemotaxis of leucocytes

(b) *Endogenous mediators* are more important in inflammation and induce Vascular permeability changes; attraction of leucocytes; activation of leucocytes; contraction of smooth muscle; dilation of blood vessels; pain and swelling

Mediator	Main source
Histamine	Mast cells or basophils
Kinins (e.g. bradykinin Kallidin leucokinins)	From blood precursors by proteases and leucocytes
Prostaglandins (E_1 & E_2) and acidic lipids	Polymorphonuclear leucocytes, monocytes and eosinophils
Slow reacting substances	Mast cells and basophils
Complement components (anaphylatoxin chemotaxins)	Derived by activation of classical or alternative pathways (Fig. 5.1)
Components of clotting system and their degradation products (fibrinopeptides)	Blood and tissue fluids
Cytokines (chemotactic factors, macrophage activating factors, mitogenic factors etc.)	Lymphocytes and macrophages

THE COMPLEMENT SYSTEM

The serum proteins that make up the complement system, which has nineteen components, play a role in both inflammation and immunity. Several components are enzymes that act on other components in sequence cleaving them into small and large fragments that have various biological activities.

There are two pathways leading to activation of the system—the **classical pathway** and the **alternative pathway** (Fig 5.1)

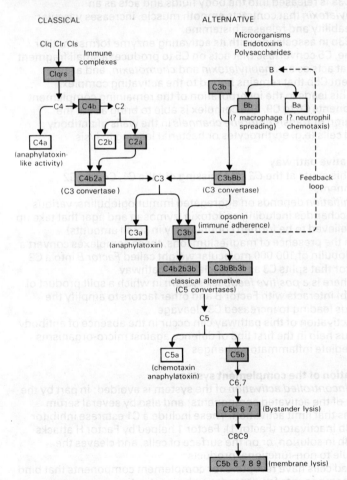

Fig. 5.1 Simplified view of activation of complement pathways and activities of components. Shaded boxes indicate components involved in completion of cascade.

Classical pathway

1. The *first component C1* is a complex of three subcomponents q, r and s. C1q is made up of six subunits with globular heads connected to a collagen like stem and interacts with the second constant domain of the antibody molecule.

2. C1s then acts on the C2 and C4 glycoproteins resulting in a complex called *C3 convertase* (C4bC2a).

3. The convertase acts on C3 and splits it into a small C3a and a large C3b subunit.

4. C3a is released into the body fluids and acts as an *anaphylatoxin* that contracts smooth muscle, increases vascular permeability and releases histamine.

5. C3b in association with its activating enzyme forms another enzyme, C5 convertase that acts on C5 to produce: a small fragment C5a that acts as an *anaphylatoxin* and *chemotaxin*; and a large fragment C5b that remains bound to the activating complex.

6. This leads to the incorporation of the remaining complement components C6 to C9. The complex is able to bring about the formation of *transmembrane channels* in the walls of antibody coated cells (e.g. erythrocytes or bacteria) leading to lysis.

Alternative pathway

1. This starts at the *C3 step* missing out the C1, C4 and C2 components

2. *Initiation* depends on aggregated immunoglobulins, various polysaccharides including endotoxin, zymosan and agar that take up C3b (believed to be formed continuously in small amounts)

3. In the presence of magnesium ions, these complexes convert a beta globulin of 100 000 molecular weight called *Factor B* into a C3 activator that splits C3 as in the classical pathway

4. There is a *positive feedback system* in which a split product of C3 (C3b) interacts with Factor B and other factors to amplify the stimulus leading to increased C3 cleavage

5. Activation of this pathway can occur in the absence of antibody and thus help in the first line of defence against micro-organisms and mediate inflammatory changes

Regulation of the complement system

1. *Uncontrolled activation* of the system is avoided: in part by the lability of the activated components; and also by several serum proteins that limit activation. These include a C1 esterase inhibitor and C3b inactivator (Factor 1). Factor 1 helped by Factor H attacks free C3b in solution, or on the surface of cells, and cleaves the molecule to non-functional products

2. Red cells have receptors for complement components that bind active components for *degradation* by inactivating enzymes

3. Human serum also contains an **anaphylatoxin inactivator** that destroys C3a, C4a and C5a

Biological effects of activation products of the complement system

Complexes and components involved	Activities
C1,4	Neutralization of *herpes simplex* virus together with IgM
C1,2,4	Possible generation of kinins, increase in vascular permeability
C3b	Immune adherence, C3b on red blood cells (rbc), white blood cells or platelets adheres to normal rbcs—agglutination *in vitro* Viruses coated with Ig and complement adhere to platelets or rbcs resulting in removal by phagocytes
C3a	Anaphylatoxin (contaction of smooth muscle, increased vascular permeability and histamine release)
C3e[1]	Mobilization of leucocytes (leucocyte promoting factor)
C3b, C5a	Simulation of oxidative metabolism of phagocytes
C5a	Leucocyte chemotaxis Anaphylatoxin Adherence of leucocytes to vascular endothelium
C5-9	Lysis of susceptible bacteria or cells
C8,9	Cytotoxic effect

[1]C3e appears to be derived from C3c by proteolytic cleavage which is itself derived from C3b by the action of β 1H globulin and the C3b activator

CLINICAL CONSIDERATIONS

1. **Deficiencies** of the later complement components **C5 to C9** are associated with recurrent or disseminated gonorrhoea and meningococcal infections
2. **Deficiency of C2** is associated with a number of disease states including systemic lupus erythematosus, polymyositis and glomerulonephritis
3. **Deficiency of C1 esterase** leads to hereditary angioneurotic oedema
4. **Deficiency** of any of the early components **C1 to C4** is associated with immune complex disease (Ch. 8)
5. **Lack** of an inhibitor—**alpha-1-antitrypsin** — for one of the mediators of the inflammatory response, elastase (from leucocyte lysosomes) is associated with emphysema
6. **Carcinoid syndrome,** a gut neoplasm, is associated with the excessive production of prostaglandins, bradykinin and 5-hydroxy tryptamine, which leads to paroxysmal flushing of the skin of the face and neck and sometimes heart valvular disease

7. **Amyloid proteins** can be deposited in various organs during chronic inflammatory processes
8. **Fibrosis,** as a result of chronic inflammation, can sometimes lead to disease: for example, cirrhosis of the liver, chronic pyelonephritis, rheumatoid joints and pyloric stenosis
9. **Chronic granulomatous disease** is due to failure of oxidative metabolism in neutrophils—several genetic forms exist
10. **Neutropenia** is a frequent side-effect of chemotherapy for malignant disease and sometimes of treatment with other drugs, such as sulphonamides
11. **Deficiency of complement receptors** — e.g. C3 receptors on red cells—is sometimes found in autoimmune diseases (Ch. 9), such as systemic lupus erythematosus, and may lead to failure to inactivate complement components

6. Infection and immunity

Most normal healthy individuals have many microorganisms living on their skin (10^{12}) and in their gut etc. (10^{14}) and are host to at least 150 types of viruses, without suffering from any detectable illness. This harmless association between host and organism is termed **commensal**, where the organism derives benefit without harming the host. A harmful association, where the organism benefits at the expense of the host is termed *parasitic*. A mutually beneficial association is termed *symbiotic*, where both host and organism gain positive benefits from the association.

NORMAL HUMAN COMMENSAL FLORA

External surfaces—skin etc.
NOSE & NASAL PHARYNX
Staphylococci
Diphtheroids
Neisseria sp
Haemophilus sp

OROPHARYNX
Staphylococci
Streptococcus sp
Neisseria sp
Haemophilus sp

MOUTH
Staphylococci
Streptococci
Actinomyces sp
Haemophilus sp
Yeasts
Enteric bacteria
Anaerobic bacteria
Spirochaetes

SKIN
Staphylococci
Streptococci
Corynebacterium
Propionibacterium
Yeasts
Diphtheroids
Enteric bacteria (rare)

Gastrointestinal system
STOMACH
Normally sterile

SMALL INTESTINE
Lactobacilli
Enterococci
Diphtheroids
Yeasts (*Candida*) } Small numbers
Enteric bacteria
Anaerobic gram
negative bacilli

LARGE INTESTINE
Anaerobic bacteria
  gram negative
    Bacteroides spp
    Fusobacterium spp
  gram positive
    Eubacterium spp
    Lactobacilli
    Clostridium spp
    Bifidobacterium
    Streptococci

Facultative and aerobic organisms
  Staphylococci
  Enterococci
  Enteric bacteria
  Proteus spp
  Pseudomonas spp
  Yeasts (*Candida*)

Genitourinary tract
KIDNEYS AND BLADDER
Normally sterile

VAGINA AND CERVIX
Anaerobic bacteria
  Lactobacilli
  Streptococci

Bacteroides spp
Clostridium spp
Bifidobacterium
Eubacterium

Aerobic bacteria
  Diphtheroids
  Staphylococci
  Enterococci
  Strep. pyogenes (group B)
Enteric bacteria

Yeasts
  Candida
Protozoa
  Trichomonas vaginalis
  (10–15% normal women)

Such organisms can become what are called **opportunist pathogens** when host defence mechanisms become compromised.

The compromised host
Compromised defences can be brought about by a variety of causes including medical or surgical intervention, environmental factors (such as drug abuse) and primary and secondary abnormalities of the immune system.

Predisposing factor	Effect on the immune system	Type of infection
Drug or X-rays in immunosuppression Allograft recipients (renal, bone marrow, heart)	Diminished cell-mediated and humoral immunity	Lung infections, bacteraemia, fungal infections, urinary tract infections
Virus immunosuppression, e.g. rubella, herpes. EB virus, hepatitis virus, HTLV 3 virus	Replication of virus in lymphoid cells with resulting impaired function	Secondary bacterial infections (also fungal and protozoal in AIDS)
Tumours	Replacement of cells of immune system	Bacteraemia, pneumonia, urinary tract infections
Malnutrition	Lymphoid hypoplasia Decrease in circulating lymphocytes Decreased phagocytic ability	Measles, tuberculosis, respiratory infections, gastrointestinal infections

Predisposing factor	Effect on the immune system	Type of infection
Smoking, inhalation of dust particles (e.g. silica, fungal spores)	Inflammatory lung changes, immune complex deposition to fungal spores	Chronic respiratory infections, allergic responses
Chronic endocrine disease (e.g. diabetes)	Decreased phagocytic activity	Staph. infections Tuberculosis Respiratory infections, bacteraemia etc.
Primary immune deficiency (see Ch. 7)	Diminished cell-mediated and/or humoral immunity	

INNATE HOST DEFENCE MECHANISMS

Determinants
1. Marked differences exist between species and strains—e.g. the rat is strikingly insusceptible to diphtheria, whilst the quinea pig and man are highly susceptible; humans are susceptible to the common cold but dogs are not, and dogs are highly susceptible and have little resistance to distemper virus, whilst man is insusceptible.
2. Poor nutrition is assocciated with impaired phagocytic activity and leucopenia and this leads to reduced resistance to infection
3. Infections are more severe at the extremes of life: due to immaturity of the immune system in the young; and to physical abnormalities, such as enlarged prostate, in the elderly
4. Hormonal abnormalities—as in diabetes, hypothyroidism and adrenal dysfunction—result in decreased resistance to infection

Mechanical barriers and secretions
1. Intact skin and mucous membranes offer **physical** barriers to micro-organisms
2. Drying of skin surface and desquamation of the superficial layers of the skin result in **shedding** of associated microorganisms
3. Damp surfaces of the mucous membranes **trap** bacteria and cilia of the lower respiratory tract **sweep** them out (mucociliary escalator)
4. The flow of fluids (such as urine) **sweep-away** micro-organisms and salivation, lacrimation and sneezing have similar effects
5. Sweat and sebaceous secretions contain **antimicrobial** *substances* (e.g. lactic acid, uric acid, ammonia, caproic acid and saturated C7, C9 and C11 fatty acids) and have a low pH (5.5) that affects the viability of many microorganisms

6. Mucous secretions also contain **antimicrobial** factors—e.g. lvsozyme lactoferrin, alpha-1 antitrypsin and IgA.
7. The normal flora produce factors that control the growth of other bacteria:
   (a) *Proprionibacterium acnes* produces **lipids** active against *Staph lococcus aureus* and *Strept ococcus pyogenes*
   (b) Normal gut bacteria occupy sites on the surface of the mucous membranes, thus **blocking** access to potential pathogens as well as using up essential nutrients that the pathogens need for their growth.
   (c) Anaerobic bacteria of the gut retard growth of salmonella and shigella species by production of **fatty acids**
   (d) Gut anaerobes deconjugate **bile acids** that are inhibitory for a variety of potential pathogens.
   (e) In the vagina, lactobacilli produce an acid that has **antimicrobial** activity. There is also oestrogen controlled **shedding** of the squamous epithelium.

Bactericidal substances of the body fluids

1. **Lysozyme**—a mucolytic enzyme found in high concentrations in neutrophils and most body fluids, except the CSF, sweat and urine. The enzyme acts on the cell wall of gram-positive bacteria resulting in lysis
2. Milk and saliva contain a **lactoperoxidase** system that has antimicrobial activity
3. **Beta-lysin** is a cationic protein from platelets that acts against gram-positive bacteria
4. A variety of **basic proteins** derived from cells damaged in an inflammatory response—e.g. protamine, histone, spermine and spermidine—have antimicrobial activity
5. **Lactoferrin** in secretions binds iron and deprives bacteria of this nutritional requirement
6. Human milk contains a **lipase** that is inhibitory to some protozoal pathogens
7. **Gastric acid** is microbicidal

Phagocytosis

1. Phagocytic cells—both of the polymorphonuclear granulocyte series, e.g. the neutrophil; and of the monocyte series, e.g. macrophages—play a very important role in removing micro-organisms that enter the tissues and fluids
2. Their oxygen dependent and independent microbicidal systems kill and degrade micro-organisms (see Ch. 5)
3. Neutrophils solubilize and remove cellular debris at the site of an inflammatory response
4. Macrophages play an important role in the initiation of the immune response by presenting antigens of micro-organisms to helper T-lymphocyte (see Ch. 4)

5. Macrophages produce a variety of mediators (such as IL-1), colony stimulating factors and prostaglandins that regulate the immune response (see Ch. 4)

The complement system (Ch. 5)
1. Activation of either the *classical pathway* by antibody antigen complexes or the *alternate pathway* by polysaccharides (such a bacterial endotoxin or yeast cell walls) results in generation of chemotactic agents for phagocytes and lytic factors that destroy microorganisms
2. Complement components can activate the antimicrobial actions of phagocytes and possibly generate kinins, which cause increases in vascular permeability so that antimicrobial factors and cells can migrate to the site of infection

INFECTION

1. Attachment
A prerequisite for infection to take place on the mucosal surfaces is attachment to the epithelial cells. Certain bacteria are adapted to do this—for example, *Salmonella typhi* attaches to the intestinal mucosa; *Corynebacterium diptheriae* to the pharyngeal mucosa; *Neisseria gonorrhoeae* to cervical epithelium; and various streptococci to either teeth or buccal mucosa.

Mechanisms
(a) The receptor sites on cells may be carbohydrate in nature, as a number of simple sugars can inhibit bacterial attachment
(b) Some bacteria have lectin (sugar recognizing) molecules in their cell walls
(c) Hair like fimbriae of bacteria assist in the attachment of many gut bacteria—for example, *E. coli* and Salmonella species
(d) Similar fimbriae (or pili) are found on pathogenic gonococci.
(e) Some species (e.g. Shigellae) penetrate epithelial cells by a process of endocytosis and are protected within the cell from the immune response. Other pathogens that are taken in by endocytosis are: protozoa, fungi, *Listeria monocytogenes* and *Neisseria gonorrhoeae*
(f) Many viruses have surface components that enable them to attach to their target cells—e.g. influenza viruses have a haemagglutinin that attaches to sialic acid on host cell membranes. The HTLV 3 virus of AIDS attaches to the T4 antigen of helper T lymphocytes

2. Evasion
Many micro-organisms have developed strategies that enable them to escape both the innate or acquired immune response:

Micro-organism	Product or characteristic	Effect
Staphylococci	Catalase	Protect from phagocyte H_2O_2
	Protein A	Binds antibody and interferes with opsonization
	Peptidoglycan	Inhibition of leucocyte migration
	Capsular material	Interference with opsonization
	Leucocidin	Cytotoxic and leucotoxic
	Haemolysin	Leucotoxic
	Coagulase	? inhibition of phagocytosis
Streptococci	Capsular polysaccharide	Inhibition of phagocytosis
	Streptolysins	Cytotoxic, inhibits chemotaxis, inhibition of macrophage migration ? inhibit lymphocyte proliferation
Gonococci and meningococci	IgA proteases	Digests and inactivates IgA
Trypanosomes, malaria parasites	Change membrane components in successive generations	Renders immune response to earlier generation ineffective
Intracellular organisms (tubercle bacilli, brucella, viruses)	Ability to survive within cells	Avoid destruction by antibody

3. Interference

Some micro-organisms, particularly viruses, disable the immune system by, for example, invading lymphocytes or macrophages and impairing their normal functions. The HTLV 3 or lymphadenopathy associated virus of AIDS is an example of this.

Micro-organisms that interfere with induction of acquired immunity

Microorganism	Effect
Measles, rubella, herpes, hepatitis viruses Lymphadenopathy associated virus of AIDS	Infection of cells of immune system and interference with induction of acquired immunity and expression of cell-mediated immunity
Malaria parasites	Depressed lymphocyte responsiveness to mitogens and some antigens

Microorganism	Effect
Leprosy bacilli	Alteration in T:B cell ratio with reduction in expression of complement receptors (? blocked by immune complexes)
	Non-specific impairment of cell-mediated immune response
Trichophyton fungi	Repeated exposure to tricophyton leads to relative allergy to the fungal antigens and reduced inflammatory response
Schistosomes	Incorporate host antigens and prevent recognition of their antigens
Influenza viruses	Suppress mitogenic responses of lymphocytes
	? Disables macrophages leading to secondary bacterial infection
Herpes simplex and cytomegalovirus	Induce Fc receptors on infected cell that bind and thus inactivate antiviral antibody

ACQUIRED IMMUNITY

Both forms of acquired immunity are involved—humoral and cellular.

Humoral Immunity

Bacterial infections
1. Antibody can neutralize bacterial toxins from e.g. diphtheria, cholera, tetanus and botulism organisms
2. Antibody can attach to the surface of bacteria and:
   (a) Act as an opsonin enabling phagocytosis, e.g. IgG and IgM
   (b) Prevent the adherence of micro-organism to their target cell e.g. IgA in the gut
   (c) Activate the complement system leading to bacterial lysis
   (d) Clump bacteria (agglutination) leading to phagocytosis
   (e) Attach bacteria to host red blood cells or platelets by Fc receptors, so that the complex is phagocytosed (immune adherence)
   (f) Inhibit the uptake of iron by bacteria by preventing bacteria from releasing their iron binding compounds
   (g) IgE attached to mast cells interacts with microbial surface to cause histamine release with inflammatory response and elimination of micro-organism (if this occurs excessively, it can lead to hyersensitivity—Ch. 8)
   (h) Inhibits motility and possibly the metabolic activity of bacteria

Virus infections
1. Antibodies can prevent attachment of viral particles to their target cells and neutralize the virus
2. Antibodies attached to the surface of enveloped viruses can activate the complement system and lead to lysis
3. Viruses coated with antibody and complement will be phagocytosed
4. Antibodies that bind to viral antigens expressed on infected cells can lead directly to lysis with complement or enable macrophages and other killer cells (p. 10) to attach by their Fc receptors and kill the infected cell
5. Virus infected cells can activate the alternative complement pathway and lead to cell lysis
6. Some viruses can activate the alternative pathway directly without antibody but this may not be sufficient to kill the virus unless antibody is also present

CELLULAR IMMUNITY

Bacterial infections
1. Bacteria that live within macrophages—e.g. tubercle bacilli, Brucellae, Listeriae—can be killed if the macrophages are activated by macrophage activating factor produced by lymphocytes (p. 11)
2. In chronic bacterial infections the organisms can be isolated in a granuloma and walled off by fibrosis

Virus infections
1. This form of immunity is the main mechanism in recovery from virus infections
2. Cytotoxic T lymphocytes recognize viral antigens on the surface of an infected cell in association with Class 1 MHC antigen (p. 27). This leads to lysis of the cell
3. Natural killer cells (NK)—origin unknown but not conventional T or B cells—are activated by interferon from macrophages and kill virus infected cells
4. T-lymphocytes that mediate delayed hypersensitivity, probably help in the early stages of a virus infection by attracting macrophages and other T-cells to the site of infection
5. Interferon produced by T-lymphocytes and a variety of other cells is released early in a virus infection (before antibody) and has an antiviral effect

SUMMARY OF IMMUNE RESPONSE TO MICRO-ORGANISMS

INDUCTION STAGE
1. Microbe breaks through innate immune mechanisms and is taken up by *INDUCER* cell (macrophage, dendritic cell)

2. Microbial antigens (processed) associated with MHC product for presentation to T-helper (Th) cells (Th cells have receptors that recognize macrophage associated antigen)

3. Interleukin-1 from macrophage stimulates Th which produce receptors for Interleukin-2

4. B-lymphocytes can also present certain types of antigen to Th cells

EFFECTOR STAGE—humoral and cell-mediated immunity

1. Macrophage interferon produced—stimulates natural killer cells that attack virus infected cells and prevents viral infection of contiguous cells

2. Interleukin-2 from Th cells stimulates formation of Tc cells that kill virus infected cells and stimulates formation of Tdh cells that produce lymphokines—e.g. chemotactic factor and macrophage activating factor that attract cells and activate macrophages to kill intra cellular organisms

3. Ts cells stimulated to regulate response

4. B-cells stimulated by lymphokines (e.g. B-cell growth factor) to produce antibody

5. Antibody kills micro-organisms with complement, brings about opsonisation and phagocytosis and coates the virus infected cell so that cells with Fc receptors (e.g. macrophages and killer cells) can destroy the infected cell (IgG, IgM)

IgA prevents adherence of microorganism to mucosal surfaces and IgE recruits inflammatory cells by releasing mediators from mast cells

SUMMARY OF THE IMMUNE DEFENCE MECHANISMS

Immune mechanisms with examples of micro-organisms of toxins against which they are effective:

Defence Mechanism	Examples of microorganisms or toxins
Surface barriers of skin and mucous membranes Stratum corneum of skin, mechanical and shedding Damp surfaces of mucous membranes and cilia (mucociliary escalator)	
	Opportunist pathogens
Microbicidal secretions on surface (long chain fatty acids) and in tissue fluids (lysozyme, basic polypeptides). Fluid flow (urine), Commensal bacteria: occupy sites, secrete antimicrobial substances, use up nutrients	

Defence Mechanism	Examples of microorganisms or toxins
Polymorphonuclear neutrophils and antibody acting as opsonin	*Streptococcus pneumoniae, Strept ococcus A or B Staphyl ococcus aureus, Haemophilus influenzae*, Neisseria and Gram-negative bacilli
Antibody (IgA or IgG) acting directly on a micro-organism or its toxin by blocking attachment to target cell and either lysing the bacteria with complement or neutralizing the toxin	Diptheria toxin Tetanus toxin Enteric pathogens (probably) *Neisseria meningitidis Neisseria gonorrhoeae* (some strains), virus infections
Antibody and cell mediated immunity acting together	*Treponema pallidum* Salmonella infections Listeria infections
Cell mediated immunity	Tubercle bacilli Leprosy bacilli, opportunist pathogens, virus infections

CLINICAL CONSIDERATIONS

Bacterial infections
1. The immune response to bacterial antigens that **cross-react** with host tissue components can cause tissue damage:-
    (a) Group A streptococal antigens cross-react with a glycoprotein of heart valves and the sarcolemma of cardiac and skeletal muscle, which can lead to *rheumatic heart disease*
    (b) Group A streptococcal antigens cross-react with a glycoprotein of the *glomerular basement membrane*
    (c) Group A streptococcal hyaluronidase cross-reacts with *synovial membrane* antigens
    (d) Group A streptococcal antigens cross-react with brain antigens and the immune response can result in *Sydenhams chorea*
2. Bacterial antigens can associate with the **surface** of host cells and result in harmful antibody-antigen interactions:
    (a) Mycoplasma organisms attach to erythrocyte membranes with resulting *haemolytic anaemia*
    (b) Antigens of *salmonella gallinarum* attach to chicken erythrocytes with a similar effect

3. Complexes of bacterial antigens and antibody (immune complexes—Type-3 hypersensitivity are commonly involved in **disease pathogenesis,** for example:

Microorganism	Mechanism	Effects
Streptococcus viridans Staphlococcus aureus enterococci etc	Discharge of microorganism from endocardium (e.g. valve surface) Complexes of bacteria and antibody localize in glomeruli, ocular fundi, beneath fingernails, in splenic macrophages	Endocarditis Focal nephritis Splenomegaly etc.
Hepatitis B	Equivalent to chronic serum sickness	Jaundice, polyarthritis, glomerulonephritis, polyarteritis etc.
Streptococcus pyogenes	Related to specific strains infecting throat or skin	Glomerulonephritis
Malaria parasite	Associated with high antibody levels to parasite antigens, complexes localize in glomerular capillary walls	Nephrotic syndrome
Mycobacterium Leprae	Arthus type immune reactions in skin. Immune complexes in joints and kidneys	Erythema nodosum in skin

4. Cell mediated delayed **hypersensitivity** reaction can lead to *fibrosis* and *cavitation* in the lungs of tuberculous patients and in leprosy to *peripheral neuropathy*

Virus infections
1. Production of antibodies against host antigens **autoantibodies** — occurs in *hepatitis B* and *Epstein Barr virus* infections. This is probably due to interference with suppressor T-cell function and consequent loss of tolerance to self
2. **Immune complexes** to viral antigens can have similar effect as in bacterial infections noted above
3. Antibody attached to viral antigens on host cells may **mask the infected cells** from the possibly helpful effect of cytotoxic T-cells
4. Experimental models in mice suggest that cell mediated reactions against virus infected **brain cells** can lead to *encephalitis* and this may occur in man
5. Cell mediated responses to viral antigens are probably responsible for the *skin rashes* associated with viral infections
6. Viruses that affect the cells of the immune system can prevent the cells carrying out their normal functions—e.g. the retrovirus

lymphadenopathy–associated virus of AIDS leads to **secondary bacterial** and **fungal infections** and infections by unusual organisms, such as *pneumocystis* and *giardia* as well as *Kaposi's sarcoma*

7. New developments in **protection from virus infection** have arisen from studies in AIDS showing that inhibitors of reverse transcriptase (e.g. suramin, antimoniotungstate and phosphonoformate) may be useful particularly in the early AIDS-related complex state of the disease. Monoclonal antibodies against the T4 receptor on helper T cells may also prevent atachment of the virus, and endocytosis of the virus might be prevented by a drug like amantadine. Ribavirin affects viral messenger RNA and is active against a range of RNA viruses

Fungal and other parasitic infections

1. **Farmer's lung** results from fungal—*Micropolyspora faeni*—infection with immune complex formation
2. **Allergic bronchopulmonary aspergillosis** can occur in patients who develop IgE antibodies to aspergillus antigens
3. Circulating immune complexes with **parasite antigens** of malaria, trypanosomes and schistosomes contribute substantially to the pathogenesis of the diseases
4. Cell mediated immunity to such **parasite antigens** can also cause *tissue damage*—for example, in schistosome infections, portal fibrosis and pulmonary hypertension are related to immune responses to eggs in the tissues
5. **Malaria** (and many other) parasites can bring about *immunosuppression*, the extent paralleling the degree of parasitaemia

IMMUNIZATION AGAINST INFECTIOUS DISEASE

Four main types of antigen preparation

1. *Toxoids*—Bacterial toxins neutralized by heat, chemical treatment (e.g. formalin), or gentle heat
2. *Killed vaccines*—organisms killed by heat, UV irradiation or chemical treatment
3. *Antigens isolated from infectious agents*—non-toxic diffusible factors, e.g. capsular antigens (rarely used)
4. *Attenuated living organisms*—made from organisms grown under unfavourable conditions with loss of virulence or related organisms, e.g. cowpox

Vaccines and recommended schedules of procedure

In special circumstances various diseases are particularly hazardous to man and protective immunization may be provided against the following:

Hazards to the fetus
Rubella
Hazards to the traveller
Enteric fever
Yellow fever
Cholera
Smallpox

Hazards associated with occupation or other special circumstances
Anthrax
Influenza
Mumps
Plague
Q fever
Rabies
Tularaemia
Typhus
Hepatitis A & B (passive immunization)
The Joint Committee on vacination and immunization (1978)
proposed the following schedule of vaccination and immunization
procedures:

Age	Vaccine	Interval	Notes
3 months	diph/tet/pert & oral polio vaccine[1] (first dose)		The first dose of triple vaccine together with oral polio vaccine should be given at 3 months. If pertussis vaccine is contraindicated or declined by parents diph/tet should be given
4½–5 months	polio vaccine[1] (second dose)	preferably after an interval of 6–8 weeks	
8½–11 months	diph/tet/pert & oral polio vaccine[1] (third dose)	preferably after an interval of 4–6 months	
During second	measles[1] year of life		
5 years of age or school entry	diph/tet oral polio[1]		
11–13 years of age	BCG		For tuberculin-negative children

Age	Vaccine	Interval	Notes
Girls between 11 and 13 years of age	rubella[1]		All girls this age should be offered rubella vaccine whether or not there is a past history of the disease
Between 15–19 years of age or on school leaving	polio (oral[1] or inactivated) & tetanus		

1 = live virus vaccines—therefore **contraindicated** during pregnancy N.B. For full details and notes the reader should refer to Protection and Prevention 6th edition, The Wellcome Medical Foundation Ltd., 1980.

Contraindications and hazards of immunization
Contraindications
1. Defer immunization if patient unwell, e.g. febrile
2. Live vaccines should not be given to patients whose immune defences are compromised
3. Live vaccines, particularly rubella, should not be given to pregnant women
4. Any history of adverse reactions to vaccines or allergy
5. Children with a history of neonatal cerebral irritation, tendency to convulsions or previous reaction to a vaccine should not receive the pertussis component of triple vaccine

Hazards
1. Minor reactions, such as local erythema and tenderness, are common
2. Fever, headache and malaise may occur, particularly with vaccines containing endotoxin
3. Allergic reactions may occur to vaccine contaminants—such as antibiotics, mercurials, or egg protein in certain viral vaccines
4. Live vaccines may contain passenger viruses—for example, polio vaccines have been implicated in transfer of SV 40 virus derived from the monkey kidney in which the polio virus was cultured

New developments
Vaccinia virus recombinants that express genes introduced from other infective agents are being tested in animals. Results indicate that protection can be achieved with influenza, herpes, rabies and vesicular stomatitis viruses in mice and hepatitis B virus in chimpanzees. Vaccinia virus is simple, economical to manufacture, relatively hazard-free and has a large capacity for foreign DNA to be inserted; thus it may lead to development of polyvalent vaccines.

7. Immune deficiency states

Recurrent, persistent or unusual infections suggest an immune deficiency state.

Indications
1. Chronic sepsis of the upper and lower respiratory tract—antibody deficiencies
2. Gastrointestinal infections (adults)—IgA antibody deficiencies
3. Arthropathy or malignant disease—occasionally
4. Generalized vaccinia after smallpox vaccination
5. Thrombocytopenia—Wiskott-Aldrich syndrome
6. Hypoparathyroidism—thymic hypoplasia

Two major categories of immune deficiency; *Primary and Secondary*. Secondary deficiencies are by far the most common.

PRIMARY IMMUNE DEFICIENCIES

World Health Organization **classification** for antibody deficiencies:
1. Transient hypogammaglobulinaemia of infancy—as maternal IgG levels fall
2. Congenital hypogammaglobulinaemia—X—linked or autosomal recessive, i.e. male infants only
3. Common variable immunodeficiency—Heterogeneous group of infants or adults
4. Immunodeficiency with raised IgM
5. Immunodeficiency with thymoma
6. Selective IgA deficiency
7. Selective IgM deficiency
8. Selective IgG subclass deficiency

Laboratory diagnosis
This depends on:
1. Estimation of *serum immunoglobulin* levels for gross or quantitative abnormalities. Even severely affected patients usually have some detectable immunoglobulin
2. Response to *test immunization* can be helpful

3. Estimation of *B-cell numbers*

Deficiencies of cell mediated immunity and humoral immunity
appear at birth or early childhood.

A summary of the main primary immune deficiency states
affecting T and B lymphocytes:

Stem cell defects	Expression	Infections
Haemopoietic stem cell (autosomal recessive)	Severe combined immune deficiency affecting T cells, B cells and phagocytes	Early onset of infections in all systems, e.g. respiratory, alimentary, skin
Lymphocyte stem cell (autosomal recessive, some X-linked)	Diminished numbers of T and B cells	
Adenosine deaminase deficiency		

T cell-defects in development

Thymus defects	1. Di George's syndrome (congenital but not usually familial (thymic hypoplasia) with diminished numbers of T cells	Recurrent viral, bacterial, fungal infections, including viral respiratory infections
	2. Ataxia Telangiectasia (autosomal recessive) affecting T cells and plasma cells—both reduced	
Defects in T cell sub populations	Variable immunodeficiencies affecting T_s or T_h cells	Viral and bacterial infections

B cell—defects in development

Arrested development at Pre- B-cell level (X-linked)	Infantile agammaglobulinaemia with diminished numbers of B cells	Mainly bacterial infections (occasional viral infections) Infection with pyogenic bacteria, if selective IgM deficiency
Defective terminal differentiation of B cells	Selective deficiency of immuno globulin classes with reduced numbers of plasma cells, B cells and sometimes T cells	

Defects in innate immune mechanisms
1. Congenital agranulocytosis
2. Chronic granulomatous disease—due to defect in NADPH pathway of neutrophils, or glucose-6-phosphate dehydrogenase deficiency
3. Defective phagocyte responses to chemotactic stimuli
4. Deficiencies of complement components (rare)—most common and severe is C3 deficiency. Sometimes associated with autoimmune diseases

SECONDARY IMMUNE DEFICIENCIES

Defects affecting lymphoid tissues
1. Infections of lymphocytes or macrophages—for example, severe immunodeficiency in infections with HTLV Type 3, or the lymphadenopathy associated virus of AIDS. Transient deficiencies in cytomegalovirus infections, infectious mononucleosis, measles, rubella and viral hepatitis. Bacterial infections such as leprosy, tuberculosis and syphilis can induce deficient function of immune system
2. Malnutrition
3. Lymphoproliferative diseases or secondary tumour deposits
4. Drugs, such as cytotoxic or immunosuppressive agents
5. Drugs that attach to leucocytes and lead to hypersensitivity reaction and leucopenia—e.g. sulphonamides
6. Antibiotics can affect neutrophil and macrophage functions—for example, chemotactic responses in neutrophils and sometimes the phagocytic function of macrophages

Loss of immunoglobulins
1. Nephrotic syndrome with loss of proteins including antibodies in the urine
2. Protein losing enteropathy—loss of immunoglobulin in the gut. This also occurs in chronic inflammatory bowel disease
3. Burns with severe loss of tissue fluids—sometimes with associated immunodepression

Types of micro-organisms involved
1. Viruses—e.g. *Herpes simplex* virus, *Varicella zoster*, cytomegalovirus
2. Bacteria—e.g. *Escherichia coli Staphlococcus aureus, Streptococcus faecalis, Pseudomonas aeruginosa, Pneumocystis carinii* and others
3. Fungi—e.g. *Candida* spp. *Aspergillus fumigatus*
4. Protozoa—e.g. *Giardia lamblia*

Management
1. Immunoglobulin replacement therapy (most common)
2. Grafting of immunocompetent cells
3. Genetic counselling
4. Antibiotic therapy
5. Possible use of Interferon and other mediators, such as Interleukin-1 and 2, as they become available through recombinant DNA technology

Indications for immunoglobulin replacement therapy
1. X-linked agammaglobuinaemia
2. Common variable agammaglobulinaemia
3. Severe combined immunodeficiency
4. Wiskott-Aldrich syndrome

Forms of replacement therapy
1. Alcohol-salt fractionated pooled human plasma (immune globulin) for intramuscular use
2. Normal human plasma. Advantages are fewer adverse reactions than immune globulin and less painful injections. Disadvantages are possible hepatitis B or HTLV 3 infection.
3. Modified (enzyme treated) immune globulin as in (1) for intravenous use. Advantage is that can be given in large doses intramuscularly with rapid action and less painful than (1). Disadvantage—rapid clearance of enzyme treated preparations from blood.

8. Hypersensitivity states

The normal acquired immune mechanisms, as has been noted in earlier chapters, perform a useful function in combating infection. However, disadvantageous reactions can unfortunately occur at the same time. For example, the release of inflammatory mediators that, whilst often helpful in bringing phagoytes serum antibody, or complement to the site of infection, can also cause damage to tissue cells. Even cellular immune reactions can result in the destruction of host cells. These disadvantageous reactions are called **hypersensitivity reactions** or **allergies.**

CLASSIFICATION OF ALLERGIC DISEASES

Allergic diseases have been classified by Gell and Coombs into four types:

Type 1
IgE antibodies attached to mast cells react with antigen (sometimes called *allergen*) and trigger the release of histamine, a slow-reacting substance of anaphylaxis and eosinophil chemotactic factor. This is the mechanism of many of the *common forms of allergy*—such as hay fever, asthma and urticaria

Type 2
IgM or IgG antibodies react with antigen (often a drug or microbial product) attached to tissue cells, such as leucocytes or erythrocytes. This results in *complement activation* and *lysis* of the cell.

Type 3
IgM or IgG antibodies form complexes with antigen and activate complement. Chemotactic factors and other inflammatory mediators are generated and tissue damage results. This is some times called *immune complex disease* and is responsible for vasculitis and kidney damage.

Type 4
Sensitised T-lymphocytes interact with antigen—for example, products of mycobacteria, or sometimes even simple chemicals attached to body proteins. Lymphokines are released and can cause inflammation. These reactions are sometimes called *delayed*

hypersensitivity responses or *contact dermatitis* when simple chemicals are involved.

HYPERSENSITIVITY STATES

In some hypersensitivity states more than one of the above types may be involved. Clinical manifestations can be modified by non-immunological factors, such as infections, emotions and drugs.

Type 1 hypersensitivity

Mechanisms
Strong family clustering possibly due to enhanced absorption of antigens or processing before presentation to IgE antibody producing cells

Inducing agents
   1. Antigens are often *inhalents*—such as, pollens, fungal spores, animal danders and dusts containing, for example, house mite antigens
   2. Antigens taken in from the gut (*ingestants*)—such as nuts, fish, milk products, food additives—in sensitive individuals can lead to allergic symptoms, such as asthma or urticaria
   3. Skin contact with antigens—often simple chemicals that attach to tissue proteins and lead to localized urticaria or sometimes systemic symptoms

Pharmacological mediators
1. Histamine
2. 5-hydroxy tryptamine (serotonin)
3. Slow reacting substance of anaphylaxis (SRS-A)
4. Platelet activating factor (PAF)
5. Chemotactic factors for neutrophils and eosinophils
6. Leucotrienes and prostaglandins

Effects
1. Mast cell mediators—increased vascular permeability, vasodilation, smooth muscle contraction and bronchial constriction
2. Eosinophil mediators—histaminase, aryl sulphatase (for SRS-A), phospholipase D (for PAF)

Summary of possible methods of immunological intervention in IgE-mediated allergy
1. Prevention of allergen reacting with IgE on mast cells by inducing high levels of allergen-specific IgG (blocking antibody) by injection of small doses of allergen. (IgG – allergen complexes may also have negative feedback affect on IgE synthesis)

2. Tolerance induction to allergen—blockade of B lymphocytes or induction of T suppressor cells
3. Induction by adjuvants of non-antigen specific suppressor factors—may be Fc receptors for IgE and so prevent IgE binding to such receptors on mast cells
4. Switching off of IgE production by antibodies against IgE idiotypic determinants (p. 18). This can be achieved by repeated injection of allergen, immunization with either Ig myeloma protein or cells carrying idiotypic determinants
5. Pharmacological interference with formation or release of inflammatory mediators (e.g. histamine, SRS-A anaphylatoxins)

Note: (1) and (5) are most commonly practised

Type 2 Hypersensitivity

Initiated by antibody reacting with antigenic determinants present on tissue cells (microbial antigens or drugs) or incompatible transfused (or grafted) cells. Occurs in organ specific autoimmune diseases (Ch. 9).

Mechanisms
1. Cell lysis by complement activation
2. Phagocytosis by opsonins
3. Killing by non-phagocytic mechanism—antibody dependent cell mediated cytotoxicity by polymorphs, monocytes and natural killer cells (p. 10)

Examples
1. In incompatible transfusion reactions mismatched erythrocytes are attacked by isohaemagglutinins (A persons have anti-B; B persons have anti-A; O persons have both; and AB persons have none). Therefore mismatched rbcs cause transfusion reactions.
2. Drug reactions can occur e.g. haemolytic anaemia can occur after treatment with chlorpromazine or phenacitin due to antibody responses to complexes of the drug and cell surface components
3. After Mycoplasma pneumonia infections—cold-haemagglutinins are produced that shorten the half life of the red cells
4. Autoimmune thyroid disease with antibodies cytotoxic for thyroid cells

Type 3 hypersensitivity

Immune complexes may be formed locally or systemically. The outcome depends on the relative proportions and on the amount of complexes formed:

1. Antibody excess to slight antigen excess—complexes tend to localize at site of formation
2. With greater antigen excess—soluble complexes form and circulate and are deposited widely, e.g. kidneys or joints

Mechanisms
1. *Acute inflammatory reactions* with fixation of complement—possible lyis of nearby cells by C5–9 'reactive lysis'
2. *Release of mediators*—anaphylatoxins, histamine, chemotactic factors, mediators from neutrophil granules
3. *Platelet aggregation* with release of vasoactive amines and the possible formation of microthrombi

Examples
   1. *Arthus reaction*—in skin—for example, in diabetics sensitised to insulin by repeated injection; and possibly other sites, such as lung, after exposure to mouldy hay or joints in rheumatoid arthritis (p. 66)
   2. *Local release of antigens* from infectious agents, such as worms, or after destruction of microbes by antibiotics with the release of quantities of microbial antigens
   3. *Serum sickness*—after injections of large quantities of foreign serum
   4. *In autoimmune diseases*, such as systemic lupus erythematosus, where anti-DNA complexes are found in kidneys, small blood vessels and sometimes in the choroid plexus (Ch. 9)
   5. *After infections with 'nephritogenic' streptococci* with deposition of complexes in the kidney glomerular basement membrane
   6. *In certain virus infections*, e.g. subacute sclerosing panencephalitis of measles in infants

Type 4 hypersensitivity
Is an exaggerated form of normal cell mediated immune reaction. Erythema and induration ocurring 24–48 hours after injection of antigen into skin, as in the tuberculin or Mantoux reaction. Infiltration of mononuclear cells in contrast to the neutrophil infiltration of the Types 1–3 reactions.

Mechanisms
1. Mediators released by sensitised T-lymphocytes are largely responsible, e.g. Macrophage migration inhibition factor
2. Cytotoxic T lymphocytes

Examples
   1. *Tuberculin reaction* as noted above. This can lead to lung damage if it occurs in tuberculous patients by causing fibrosis and cavitation
   2. *Formation of granuloma* in a variety of chronic parasitic diseases
   3. *Contact dermatitis* to simple chemicals—e.g. picryl chloride, nickel, hair dyes, plant antigens (such as, poison ivy).
   4. *Insect bites*

Genetic factors in allergy

1. The IgE levels of normal individuals are low (Table 3.1) and are controlled by a dominant gene. The higher the level the greater the chance of allergic predisposition
2. Ragweed allergy is closely associated with the DW2 locus of HLA
3. Immune hyperactivity (associated with HLA-B8 and DW 3) particularly of IgE responses to a wide range of antigens is a feature of allergic individuals

Other factors include degree of exposure to allergens, nutritional state of the individual, presence of chronic infections or acute viral infections

9. Disturbances of homeostasis

A number of instances have been noted in earlier chapters where either immunoregulatory mechanisms have been disturbed by infective agents, or where the immune response occurs in an abnormal or exaggerated form to the disadvantage of the individual. A number of pathological states exist where the immune response has either failed to cope adequately with an abberent cell population (as in **malignant disease**) or become deregulated for illdefined reasons (as in **autoimmune disease**).

In **pregnancy** the fetus can be considered as an allograft with products of paternal genes displayed on the fetus. The mother's immune system does respond to these antigens but the fetus is protected by as yet illdefined mechanisms. Miscarriages tend to occur in partners who are genetically similar, suggesting that there is a positive advantage in the development of some degree of maternal immunity to the fetus.

THE RELATIONSHIP BETWEEN IMMUNE RESPONSE AND HOST TUMOURS

1. *A beneficial role of immunity is suggested by the following findings:*

    (a) Higher incidence of tumours following immunosuppression
    (b) Higher incidence of tumours in immunodeficiency states
    (c) In experimental tumours in animals, there is evidence for a role of immune mechanisms in limiting tumour growth—particularly for virally induced tumours and those induced by chemical carcinogens
    (d) Many tumours are infiltrated by lymphoid mononuclear cells

2. *These findings are taken as evidence that the immune system plays a 'surveillance' role in seeking out and destroying newly arising malignant cells.* The requirements for this are:

    (a) A clone of malignant cells must express altered self or neoantigens

   (b) Such antigens must be immunogenic and not tolerogenic
   (c) That the immune response results in production of appropriate effector mechanisms to destroy the tumour
3. *However, considerable evidence exists that*:
   (a) Many tumours are only weakly if at all antigenic and many tumours grow without any evidence of antitumour immunity
   (b) Only limited evidence that mononuclear cell infiltration affects the growth of the tumour
   (c) Tumours found in immunosuppressed or immunodeficient patients are frequently lymphoreticular cell tumours; which suggests a disturbance in regulation of lymphoid cell populations rather than a failure of immune surveillance
4. *Thus in conclusion*, it appears that most spontaneously appearing tumours are only weakly antigenic if at all and this may reflect the ability of the tumour to escape immune surveillance mechanisms. *Factors ensuring tumour survival are*:

   (a) Immunosuppressive factors produced by tumours—for example prostaglandins
   (b) Shedding of large amounts of tumour antigens can overwhelm the capacity of the immune system
   (c) Masking of tumour antigens by antibody (enhancement) so that effector cells such as cytotoxic T-cells cannot recognize the tumour cell
   (d) Modulation of tumour surface antigens in the face of an immune response—this has been observed in cultures of tumour cells grown in the presence of tumour specific antibody
   (e) Growth of the tumour in a site not accessible to cells of the immune system—immunologically privileged sites—for example, the central nervous system

Immunodiagnosis of tumours
1. Antisera raised in experimental animals against tumour antigens can be valuable as markers of tumour cells in biopsy specimens. Monoclonal antibodies are widely used for this purpose and for classification of tumours
2. Tumour products secreted into the blood are useful markers—for example, myeloma proteins and carcinoembryonic antigen

Immunotherapy of tumours
1. Generally ineffective and not the treatment of choice even combined with chemotherapy
2. Can enhance tumour growth by masking tumour antigens
3. Future use of tumour specific monoclonal antibodies (perhaps linked to a cytotoxic drug) is probably the best hope particularly in tumours of the lymphoid tissues.

AUTOIMMUNE DISEASE

There are two general categories: *organ specific diseases* and *non-organ specific diseases*

Examples of organ specific diseases

1. *Autoimmune thyroiditis* (Hashimoto's disease) with autoantibodies against thyroglobulin, cell surface and cytoplasmic thyroid antigens
2. *Autoimmune haemolytic anaemia* with antibodies against erythrocyte antigens
3. *Pernicious anaemia* with autoantibodies against vitamin B_{12} (intrinsic factor)

Examples of associations between HLA type and some diseases

Disease	HLA	Frequency % Patients	Controls
Ankylosing spondylitis	B27	90	9.4
Reiters Disease	B27	79	9.4
Acute anterior uveitis	B27	52	9.4
Subacute thyroiditis	B35	70	14.6
Idiopathic hemochromatosis	A3	76	28.2
	B14	16	3.8
Psoriasis vulgaris	CW6	87	33.1
Coeliac disease	DR3	79	26.3
Idiopathic Addison's disease	DR3	69	26.3
Insulin-dependent diabetes	DR3	56	28.2
	DR4	75	32.2
Myasthenia gravis	DR3	50	28.2
	B8	47	24.6
Systemic Lupus erythematosus	DR3	70	28.2
Multiple sclerosis	DR2	59	25.8
Rheumatoid arthritis	DR4	50	19.4
Hashimoto's thyroiditis	DR5	19	6.9
Pernicious anaemia	DR5	25	5.8

HLA = Human leucocyte antigen

Examples of non-organ specific diseases

1. *Systemic lupus erythematosus* with autoantibodies against nuclear antigens, a variety of cellular and subcellular antigens e.g. mitochondria, immunoglobulin components e.g. rheumatoid factor and cardiolipin (Wasserman antigen used for the diagnosis of syphilis). Clinical features include joint inflammation in over half of patients, skin lesions in about one fifth with haemolytic anaemia and thrombocytopenic purpura in a few patients

2. *Rheumatoid arthritis* with autoantibodies against immunoglobulin antigens (rheumatoid factor), cell nuclei, thyroid antigens, mitochondria etc. The pathogenesis has been extensively studied and serves as a useful example of non-organ specific autoimmune disease with immune complexes:

Rheumatoid arthritis
Initiating event

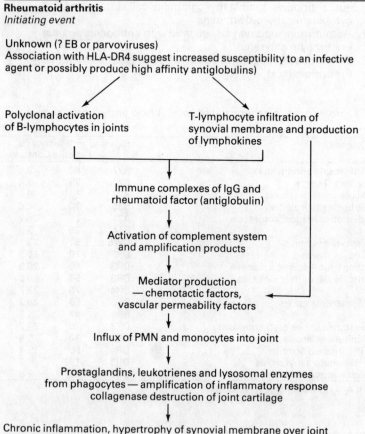

Unknown (? EB or parvoviruses)
Association with HLA-DR4 suggest increased susceptibility to an infective agent or possibly produce high affinity antiglobulins)

Polyclonal activation
of B-lymphocytes in joints

T-lymphocyte infiltration of
synovial membrane and production
of lymphokines

Immune complexes of IgG and
rheumatoid factor (antiglobulin)

Activation of complement system
and amplification products

Mediator production
— chemotactic factors,
vascular permeability factors

Influx of PMN and monocytes into joint

Prostaglandins, leukotrienes and lysosomal enzymes
from phagocytes — amplification of inflammatory response
collagenase destruction of joint cartilage

Chronic inflammation, hypertrophy of synovial membrane over joint
surfaces (pannus) with inflammatory cells releasing enzymes — destruction
of cartilage and joint deformity

Extra-articular disease is less well understood but can include anaemia, rheumatoid nodules, vasculitis, eye disease (e.g. episcleritis), nerve lesions (e.g. peripheral neuropathy), pericarditis, pleurisy, lymphadenopathy, splenomegaly and general malaise.

Between these two extremes lie a number of conditions — such as, *juvenile diabetes* with antibodies against pancreatic islet antigens and leucocyte antigens; *primary biliary cirrhosis* with antibodies against mitochondria of various cells; and *active chronic hepatitis* with antibodies against smooth muscle antigens and nuclei.

Diagnosis of autoimmune disease
The laboratory diagnosis of autoimmune disease depends upon detection of autoantibodies by immunofluorescent, immunohistochemical and radioimmunoassay methods (Ch. 10)

Factors determining self-tolerance
1. B-lymphocytes are able to recognise T-cell dependent self-antigens but without T-cell help do not produce autoantibodies. Thus self-tolerance depends mainly on T-cells
2. T-cell tolerance is believed to develop in the thymus. This will apply only to antigens that are present on thymic cells or haematogenous cells circulating through the organ
3. The fact that T-helper cells can only recognize antigen in association with Class 2 MHC molecules will prevent them responding to self-antigens on non-haematogenous cells, as they do not normally express Class 2 antigens
4. T-cell independent antigens (i.e. with multiple repeating determinants) readily induce tolerance in B-cells and induce suppressor T-cells

Aetiology of autoimmune disease
This is obscure but some possible mechanisms have been suggested that may overcome self-tolerance:
1. *Sequestered antigens* — e.g. sperm antigens that are acquired during maturation and are absent from immature germinal cells, so that tolerance does not exist. Favoured by some experimental evidence of orchitis in guinea pigs immunized with sperm and adjuvant. The orchitis following mumps infection may be due to autoimmunity
2. *Antigens shared between micro-organisms and host tissues* — e.g. streptococcal antigens and heart tissue and glomerular antigens (p. 48) An example of much interest to clinical immunologists is the association between antigens of *Klebsiella pneumoniae* and one of the human HLA haplotypes (see below) HLA B27. This haplotype is found in the majority of patients with a joint disease — ankylosing spondylitis. However, the details of the pathogenesis are not understood
3. *Drugs that bind to body proteins or cell surfaces* — e.g. a breakdown product of alpha-methyldopa (used in hypertension) may be incorporated into one of the red cell antigens (rhesus antigen) and lead to autoantibody formation

4. *Disturbed immunological regulation* — probably the most popular explanation. Chemicals, infectious agents (bacteria and viruses) are believed to upset the normal immunoregulatory mechanisms˙ so that there is a breakdown of tolerance to self-antigens (e.g. effects on suppressor T cells that normally ensure self-tolerance)

5. *Gamma interferon* produced during viral infections has been proposed as an initiating agent because it induces the expression of Class 2 MHC antigens on tissue cells not normally expressing such antigens. T-helper cells can then recognize self-antigens in association with the Class 2 antigen with resulting autoimmunity (see above). In support of this proposal, transient autoimmunity is frequently found in infective states

Genetic factors

1. Associations — some strong and some weak — have been found between certain antigens of the major histocompatibility complex (MHC) and various autoimmune diseases. The fact that some of the genes controlling these antigens (e.g. the Ir genes) determine the ability of an individual to mount an immune response and that other MHC antigens might act as receptors for viruses or other microorganisms, has led to the suggestion that these associations might shed light on the aetiology. However, there is little detailed understanding of autoimmunity. A list of some of the diseases and their association with human HLA antigens of the MHC are given above.

2. As knowledge of the extent of polymorphism in the Class 2 region in man (Fig. 4.2) increases, it should be possible to define the associations more closely

3. Recently it has become apparent that 95% of individuals with insulin dependent diabetes show an association with HLA DR3 and DR4 and the condition is negatively associated with DR2. In the congenital rubella syndrome 20% of the patients develop diabetes and they are usually DR3 positive and DR2 negative

Mechanisms of tissue damage

Hypersensitivity reactions of Types 2, 3 and 4 are those involved in the tissue damage associated with autoimmune diseases. Hypersensitivity reactions are described in Chapter 8. Rheumatoid arthritis provides an instructive example of how Type 3 hypersensitivity reactions may contribute to the pathogenesis of chronic inflammatory disease (see above).

Immunotherapy

Increasing knowledge of the details of immunoregulation and the availability of purified mediators — 1 L-1, 1 L-2, Interferons, T-cell suppressor factors, etc.—and monoclonal antibodies developed against immunoglobulin idiotypes offer the best hope for future therapy of this group of diseases. Plasmapheresis for immune-complex mediated autoimmune disease along with immunosuppressive drugs may be useful

Fetal maternal relationships

As noted above (p. 63), pregnancy in an immunological paradox in which the fetus is recognized as foreign but apparently protected by some ill-defined properties of the trophoblast from the maternal immune response to paternally derived antigens

Recent developments indicate

1. Recurrent abortions are associated with a close genetic relationship (histocompatibility antigens) between mother and father
2. Maternal antibodies to fetal antigens are produced where the parents are genetically dissimilar and appear to offer protection to the fetus (blocking antibody)
3. The incidence of recurrent abortions can be reduced by immunization of the mother by injections of paternal lymphocytes — as a source of paternal antigens

10. Immunology in diagnosis

The unique specificity of the acquired immune response and the fact that antigens and their corresponding antibodies interact by forming reversible, non-covalent links to produce complexes provide powerful laboratory tools. The development of monoclonal antibodies (Ch. 3) has revolutionized many of these tests.

TECHNIQUES AVAILABLE

There are two main types of procedures:

1. *Primary reactions*—antibody is reacted directly with antigens and these complexes are measured: by visualization as precipitates; estimation of light absorption or scattering; or measurement of radioactivity bound to the antigen or antibody reagent

2. *Secondary reactions*—another component is activated or changed, or inert particles (such as latex or red cells) are agglutinated

Examples

1. **Precipitation in gels**—This technique is a simple assay in which the antibody and antigen are allowed to diffuse towards each other in an agarose gel. Precipitation takes place as bands, which are easily seen, or sometimes augmented by a protein stain (Fig 10.1). The assay can be used to measure the amount of a particular antigen or antibody. Figure 10.2 illustrates immunoglobulin levels in serum as measured by the radial immunodiffusion assay

There are many variants of this procedure—such as immunoelectrophoresis, which combines separation of components by electrophoresis with their visualization by precipitation with specific antibodies (Fig 10.3)

2. **Nephelometry**—This is a rapid and convenient assay that depends on changes in the light scattering properties of antigen and antibody when they combine to form complexes. The light source is a helium-neon laser

3. **Radioimmunoassay**—In these assays, either antigen or antibody is labelled with a radioactive isotope, such as ^{131}I. The

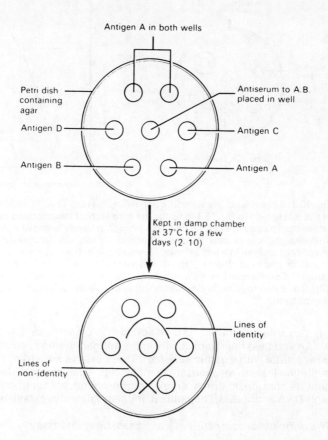

Fig. 10.1 Precipitation test in gel medium. Double diffusion test in which antigen and antibody solutions are placed in wells and then allowed to diffuse towards each other in agar or agarose gels. A concentration gradient forms and at equilibrium of the two reactants a precipitin band forms. Lines of identity form if adjacent wells contain the same antigen (A) and crossed lines (lines of non-identity) if the wells contain different antigens. Complex patterns of identity and non-identity can form with polyvalent antisera and mixtures of antigens. To make a permanent record of the bands, the gel can be dried and the bands stained. A micro version of this test uses layers of gel on a microscope slide and is more economical with the reagents than the test in a Petri dish.

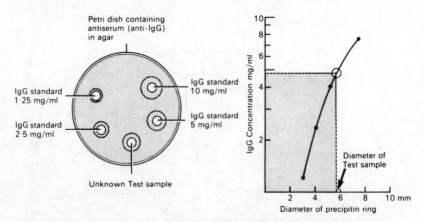

Fig. 10.2 Single radial immunodiffusion (Mancini) test. This is a modification of the test shown in Fig. 10.1 in which the antiserum is incorporated in the gel rather than placed in a central well. The precipitin bands form as rings rather than straight lines or arcs. This test is particularly valuable for measuring the quantity of antigen in a test sample. The diameter of the ring is compared to standards and read off on a graph as shown (● standards, 0 unknown test sample). Commercial kits are available for measuring the levels of the different immunoglobulin classes and other antigens, such as complement components.

labelled antigen/antibody is then added in excess to a sample of the Ab/Ag and then the radioactivety in the antigen-antibody complexes is measured with a gamma counter. These assays are widely used in inhibition tests to measure small molecules: such as, steroid and peptide hormones; drugs (digoxin or morphine); autoantibodies (anti-DNA antibodies); hepatitis B antigen; IgE and prostaglandins

The principle of competitive binding radioimmunoassay

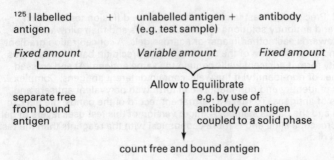

(Amount of labelled antigen bound to antibody is determined by the amount of unlabelled antigen that competes in test sample)

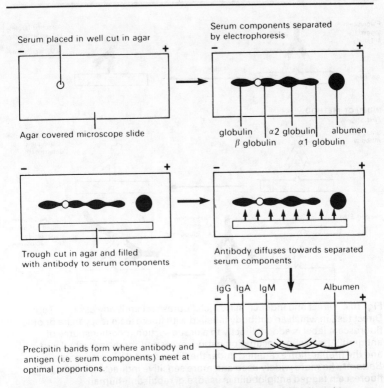

Serum placed in well cut in agar

Agar covered microscope slide

Serum components separated by electrophoresis

globulin α2 globulin albumen
β globulin α1 globulin

Trough cut in agar and filled with antibody to serum components

Antibody diffuses towards separated serum components

IgG IgA IgM Albumen

Precipitin bands form where antibody and antigen (i.e. serum components) meet at optimal proportions.

Fig. 10.3 Immunoelectrophoresis. The antigen (for example, serum) is placed in a small well cut in a layer of agar on a microscope slide. A direct current is applied and differential migration of the serum components takes place. (they are not normally visible in the agar and will show up only if suitably stained.) After electrophoresis for an hour or so, a trough is cut longitudinally in the agar and an antiserum against the electrophoresed antigen is placed in the trough. The two components diffuse towards each other and precipitin bands form. These can be shown up more clearly by staining with a protein stain. This is a very powerful analytic technique and can show up about 39 different components in human serums with 4 or 5 by electrophoresis. Various modifications are available e.g. electrophoresis in two dimensions with antiserum incorporated in the gel (rocket immunoelectrophoresis)

4. **Immunofluorescence**—In these systems, either antigen or antibody are labelled with a fluorochrome and the antigen—antibody complexes visualized with ultraviolet light. This technique is particularly valuable for detection of antigens or immune complexes in tissue sections. There are two types of immunofluorescence tests: (a) *direct* and (b) *indirect*, or *sandwich methods* (Fig 10.4)

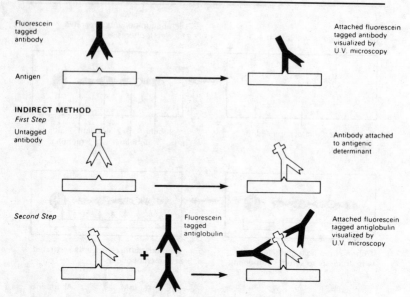

Fig. 10.4 Direct and indirect (sandwich flourescent antibody assays). *Top*: Direct test, in which an antibody labelled with fluorescein isocyanate or other fluorescent label is added directly to a tissue section (or other source of antigen). After a short incubation period, excess antibody is washed away and the preparation examined under the fluorescent (UV) microscope. *Bottom*: The more widely used and more sensitive indirect test. Here a fluorescein tagged antiglobulin is used, e.g. rabbit anti-human immunoglobulin. This reagent can be used with a variety of antibodies of the appropriate species — e.g. anti-human immunoglobulin will detect human antibodies against any antigen.

5. **Agglutination**—These are assays in which red cells or bacteria are clumped by antiserum that crosslinks antigens on the surface particles. This type of test is used for blood grouping and detection of an increase in specific antibodies to viruses or bacteria following infection (Fig 10.5). A two stage reaction is widely used—Coombs test (Fig. 10.6) Latex particles coated with immunoglobulin are used to detect rheumatoid antiglobulins (RA factor) (p. 66)

6. **Complement fixation**—Activation of complement is measured by the ability of the late components of the system (p. 35) to lyse indicator red cells coated with anti-red cell antibody (Fig 10.7)

7. **Immunoenzyme assays**—Enzyme-linked immunosorbent assay ELISA; This form of assay is similar to the fluorescent antibody technique except that the antibody is linked to an enzyme, such as horse radish peroxidase. A common form of the assay is to attach an antigen to the surface of a plastic plate (e.g. microtitre plate). Enzyme labelled antibody is then added, left to attach and the

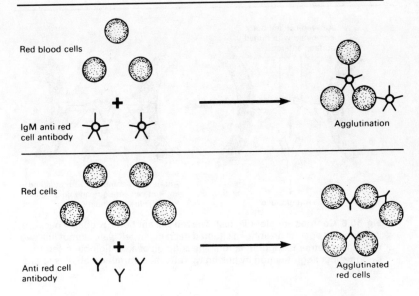

Fig. 10.5 Principle of agglutination reaction. *Top*: Immunoglobulin M with its multiple binding sites is very effective at linking particles together, such as red blood cells, as shown. The test can be quantitated by preparing dilutions of an antibody containing serum (e.g. doubling dilutions). The end-point — the last dilution giving agglutination — is called the titre and is usually expressed as the reciprocal of the dilution. *Bottom*: Immunoglobulin G can also bring about agglutination but less effectively than immunoglobulin M. Agglutination by immunoglobulin G is enhanced by the use of a developing serum — an anti-immunoglobulin (Fig. 10.6) and is used for example in testing for antibodies against rhesus antigens in haemolytic disease of the newborn. The test is often called a Coombs test.

excess washed away. The attached antibody is detected by adding the enzyme substrate and measuring the colour that develops in a spectrophotometer. This basic assay can be used to detect antigen in a test sample by adding it along with the enzyme linked antibody so that it competes for the antigen attached to the plate. Thus less antibody will be left to attach to the fixed antigen and less colour will develop on addition of the substrate. Assays of this type are used widely in the diagnostic laboratory and are under development for the diagnosis of AIDS

Cell-mediated immunity
There are also a number of assays available for measuring cell mediated responses:

1. **Lymphocyte transformation**—These measure the ability of lymphocytes to proliferate after exposure to an antigen or, more

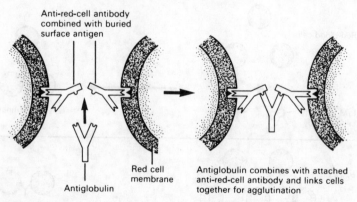

Fig. 10.6 Coombs antiglobulin test. The red cell antibody, probably because it is directed against an antigen situated deep in the cell wall, cannot link two red cells together for agglutination. The addition of an antiglobulin serum brings about agglutination by linking two attached immunoglobulins to one another

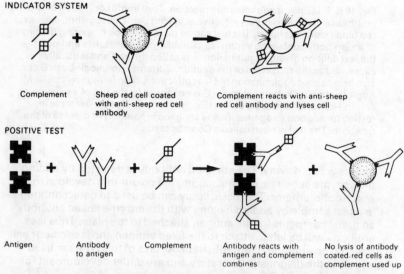

Fig. 10.7 Principle of complement fixation test. A widely used test, e.g. Wasserman test for syphilis and tests for viral antibodies. *Top*: Test uses an indicator system of sheep red blood cells coated with anti-sheep red cell antibody. The addition of complement (usually fresh guinea pig serum) to these cells brings about lysis. *Bottom*: If however, another antigen — antibody system — for example patient's serum and Wassermann antigen is first mixed with the guinea pig serum its complement will be used up (fixed) and thus not available to lyse the sheep red blood cells when they are added

commonly, to the plant mitogen phytohaemagglutinin (PHA). Proliferation is measured by incorporation of tritiated thymidine.

2. **Lysis of target cells**—Cytotoxic T-cell activity can be measured by labelling target cells with ^{51}Cr and measuring the release of the radioactivity by the lysed cells. Another method is to determine the ability of cells to exclude a dye, such as trypan blue. The target cells killed by the cytotoxic T-cells will be stained but the intact cells will not.

3. **Production of mediators from lymphocytes**—These are substances, such as the macrophage migration inhibition factors. (Fig 10.8) Interleukin-2 or interferon. Assays for these substances are very specialized and are not used routinely.

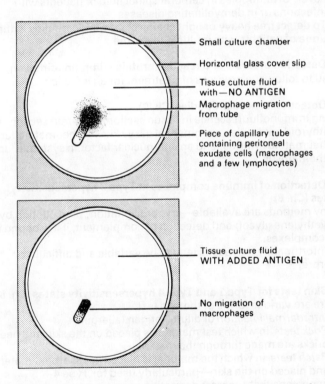

Small culture chamber

Horizontal glass cover slip

Tissue culture fluid with—NO ANTIGEN

Macrophage migration from tube

Piece of capillary tube containing peritoneal exudate cells (macrophages and a few lymphocytes)

Tissue culture fluid WITH ADDED ANTIGEN

No migration of macrophages

Fig. 10.8 Macrophage migration inhibition test. Mainly used as a test for cell mediated immunity. The test can be used quantitatively by measuring the area of migration of the macrophages. A variant of this test is used with human peripheral blood leucocytes called the leucocyte migration inhibition tests

CLINICAL APPLICATIONS

A. Quantitation of serum immunoglobulin levels (immunodiffusion)
1. Patients with severe or repeated infections—e.g., actinomycosis, subacute bacterial endocarditis, infectious mononucleosis
2. Liver disease
3. To monitor immunotherapy of patients with immunoproliferative disorders—e.g., monoclonal gammopathies of IgG, IgA or IgM (Ch. 3)
4. To distinguish transient changes, such as those following burns from primary immunodeficiencies
5. Estimation of immune responses following natural infection or immunization—IgA levels in patients with infections of mucosal surfaces or IgE levels in patients with allergies
6. Levels of antibodies in cerebral spinal fluid of patients with infections or in demyelinating diseases
7. To detect free heavy or light chains of immunoglobulins in the urine of patients with multiple myeloma

B. Detection of levels of C reactive proteins (immunodiffusion)
Used to follow the progress of treatment for an infection

C. Detection of autoantibodies (Ch. 9)
Using immunofluorescence in tissue sections—thyroid sections for antithyroid antibodies; commercial assay kits for rheumatoid factor in rheumatoid arthritis; and an anti-nuclear factor in systemic lupus erythematosus.

D. Detection of immune complexes in Type 3 hypersensitivity states (Ch. 8)
Many methods are available—cryoprecipitation; precipitation by polyethylene glycol; and detection of complement, if it is bound to the complexes.
    Unfortunately the results tend to be variable and difficult to interpret

E. Skin tests for Type 1 and Type 4 hypersensitivity states (Ch. 8)
There are various forms of the skin test:
1. *Intradermal injection* of dilute antigen (allergen)
2. *Prick tests*, in which test material is placed on the skin and needle pricks are made through the material
3. *Patch tests*, in which the material is placed in absorbent materials and placed on the skin—particularly used for Type 4 hypersensitivity contact dermatitis

F. Estimation of complement components
The most common procedure in the past was to measure total complement levels, but individual components can be measured

more conveniently with commercially available immunodiffusion plates

G. Tests of lymphocyte function
1. *Lymphocyte transformation test* (see above) used for *in vitro* test of cell mediated immunity in suspected immunodeficiency.
2. *Macrophage (leukocyte) migration inhibition test (Fig 10.8)* This is less commonly used than the transformation test above

H. Tests of phagocyte function—for suspected chronic granulomatous disease in patients with unresolving infections:
1. *Intracellular enzyme activity*—The ability to reduce the dye nitrobluetetrazolium (NBT) as an indicator of the activity of oxygen-dependent bactercidal activities
2. *Phagocytosis*—Ability to ingest inert particles (yeast or latex), opsonized red cells or bacteria to test for Fc receptor function
3. *Chemotaxis*—Ability to be attracted by a chemoattractant through a membrane filter
4. *Chemiluminescence*—emission of light by phagocytes as a test for their ability to be activated

I. Diagnosis of infection
Many of the assays described above can be used to help in the diagnosis of infection. The availability of monoclonal antibodies has brought rapid progress to this area and they can be used, for example, to identify specific microorganisms in culture or in tissues and fluids from infected patients. Complement fixation tests, virus neutralisation tests, ELISA assays, radioimmunoassay and immunofluorescence are widely used in the diagnostic laboratory. Immune complex detection can be valuable in diagnosis of bacterial endocarditis. The development of simple and highly sensitive methods for detection of nucleic acids is now being applied to diagnosis of infection using nucleic acid hybridisation and are likely to provide a valuable additional aid to immunoassays in the diagnostic laboratory

Index